Conifers Coming of Age

preceeding page: **Cedrus deodara** - Himalayan Cedar
This beautiful tree is about 50 years old. An excellent
example of Age -- This is a **mature** speciman.

Dwarf & Unusual
Conifers Coming of Age

A Guide to
Mature Garden Conifers

featuring

The Gotelli Collection
of Dwarf & Slow-Growing Conifers
The United States National Arboretum
Washington, D.C.

Sandra McLean Cutler

above: Conifer Road on an early fall morning, approaching
The Gotelli Collection of Dwarf & Slow-Growing Conifers

Dwarf & Unusual
Conifers Coming of Age
A Guide to Mature Garden Conifers

Sandra McLean Cutler

Published by
Barton-Bradley Crossroads Publishing Co.
P.O. Box 802
North Olmsted, OH 44070-0802

Publisher's Cataloging in Publication
(*Prepared by Quality Books Inc.*)

Cutler, Sandra McLean.
   Dwarf and unusual conifers coming of age : a guide to mature
garden conifers / by Sandra McLean Cutler.
   p. cm.
   Includes bibliographical references and index.
   Preassigned LCCN: 96-97053
   ISBN 0-9654717-0-5

   1. Conifers. 2. Conifers--Identification.   I. Title.

SB428.C88 1997   635.9'7752
                                         QBI96-40628
10 9 8 7 6 5 4 3 2 1
First Edition

Manufactured in Hong Kong
Color Separations by Rainbow Graphic Arts Co., Limited
Printed by Paramount Printing Company Limited

Acknowledgements

It is with my most sincere gratitude that I acknowledge the following people for their contributions:

First and foremost, this book would not have been possible without the help & cooperation, encouragement & support from Susan Martin, Curator, Gotelli, Watnong & Dogwood Collections, The U.S. National Arboretum, Washington, D.C.

Scott Aker, Integrated Pest Management Coordinator, The U.S. National Arboretum, who wrote such a thorough report, I was able to just 'land' it in the Care & Maintenance section of this book.

Ed Rezek — I am honored!

For the very helpful, realistic criticism of my first photos, and the genuinely constructive advice that made improvement possible, I must thank Charlene Harris.

Suzy Morris, my personal (or so it seemed — Are you <u>sure</u> you have other clients???) printing/publishing consultant — who doesn't know a darn thing about gardening, but sure knows her printing business! — who was there when I needed her, who got me the answers before they became problems, and who was always ready & willing to 'go the extra mile'.

The help, encouragement & support of Linda Davis, who so willingly acted as my Assistant ("I'm just reaching for my toothbrush — What date was that again?") and very best Critic.

Only someone who has been through it can know how grateful I am for the help, encouragement & support of my husband, Bob Cutler, who wanted to know exactly what I was going to give up in order to do this book!

And last, but not least, to all my special friends who so willingly took on the very last 'read' — so I could go to print with a clean conscience. Thank you!

Pinus palustris - Longleaf Pine
Early morning in March near Fern Valley.

Dedication

My mother - Madelyn McLean Cotten; my sister - Bari McLean; my friend - Susan Martin — They knew I could do it!

My husband, Bob — He hoped I could do it!

Photographs

- except where otherwise noted -
by Sandra McLean Cutler
often with the assistance of Linda Davis or Bob Cutler

Edward F. Rezek

Edward F. Rezek belongs in the "Who's Who" of dwarf & unusual conifers. He started his own conifer collecting in the early 1950's, getting advice and inspiration from collectors such as William Gotelli. He is generous in the time he gives to others, inspiring gardeners and conifer collectors the world over with his knowledge, experience and beautiful display garden. Below, I've listed a few of his `conifer contributions':

Founding member of the American Conifer Society.

Board Member, ACS, from its inception in 1983 through 1993.

Author of many articles for the ACS Bulletin.

Appeared on National television with Jim Wilson in *Victory Garden*, showing the public through his awe-inspiring garden, allowing everyone interested to see his amazing collection of dwarf and unusual conifers, and demonstrating how 'simple' it is to graft a Japanese maple.

Jim Wilson, in his book, *"Masters of the Victory Garden"*, has a chapter on dwarf conifers, written about and showing Ed Rezek's garden; again, with Ed showing how 'simple' it is to graft a Japanese maple.

Ed's conifer garden is featured in *"Specialty Gardens"* by Theodore James, Jr., a book featuring specialty gardens from around the world, with photographs by Harry Haralambou, published by Stewart, Tabori & Chang, Inc., 1992.

The February 1996 issue of *Country Living Gardener* has an article about Ed's garden, with 8 full pages in color, showing what is a city-lot-size yard impeccably landscaped with his extensive collection of conifers and companion plants. The article, "Curtain Up", starts with,

> "Welcome to the small world of Ed Rezek, acclaimed collector and breeder of dwarf conifers. In Ed's Long Island, N.Y., backyard, bird's-nest spruces, Hinoki cypresses, and weeping cedars create a fantasyland fit for an Oriental emperor."

I have been an admirer of Ed Rezek's since I first learned about him in my earliest research into dwarf conifers, when I read *"Masters of the Victory Garden"*. I was delighted to finally meet him in the Fall of '95. It is an honor to have him write the preface for this book.

Sandra McLean Cutler

Table of Contents

Preface

I first met Sandra McLean Cutler at the October - 1995 Eastern Region meeting of the American Conifer Society, held at Sherwood's Forest Nursery in Nottingham, Pennsylvania. Her enthusiasm and excitement about dwarf and unusual conifers made it a delight to listen and talk to her, inasmuch as I had been down the same road many years ago. To this day, the excitement of collecting new dwarf conifers is still there, if not more so.

It was a great pleasure to learn how she became so involved and obsessed with the dwarf conifer syndrome. She says it all started with her visit to the U.S. National Arboretum. One of the collections she visited was the Gotelli conifer collection. She was awe-struck by the beauty of these conifers; the color, shapes, foliage, textures, etc. She had no idea that conifers could look so handsome, when expertly planted and arranged in the proper setting.

I can relate to her emotions and feelings, but from a different era. In the mid Fifties, I visited Mr. Gotelli at his home in South Orange, New Jersey. At that time, I had a slight interest in conifers, but nothing compared to the interest that developed after viewing these mature conifer specimens in a magnificent garden setting. Each conifer was groomed to perfection. I had never seen a garden so beautifully designed with just dwarf and unusual conifers.

The Gotelli garden opened up a whole new vista for me. It inspired me to create something special for myself. I have derived so much pleasure over the years gardening with conifers and I truly believe it was that visit to Gotelli's garden that started me on my way.

How wonderful it is when an author like Sandra McLean Cutler can show mature dwarf and unusual conifers through her writing skills and the superb photography exhibited in the book. This is especially demonstrated by her use of the Gotelli collection as her theme. She could not have made a better choice.

Sandra's book, *"Dwarf and Unusual Conifers Coming of Age"* is the ideal book for gardeners getting involved with conifers for the first time, as well as those already involved for years. The numerous photographs provide a visual reference for mature specimens and group plantings. Ms. Cutler has done her homework well. All facets of gardening concerning conifers have been thoroughly covered: the history of the Gotelli and Watnong collections, classification of conifers, common and botanical nomenclature, growth habits, guidelines for hardiness, disease and pest control, even recommended reading lists for additional information.

Again, my thanks to Sandra McLean Cutler for bringing the Gotelli collection to the attention of budding conifer enthusiasts and those who have been established collectors. I believe that an acknowledgment of thanks and appreciation should also be extended to Susan Frost Martin, Overseer of the Gotelli collection at the United States National Arboretum, whose watchfulness and dedication has preserved and added to this most valuable collection.

Edward F. Rezek

Introduction

My introduction to the Gotelli Collection of Dwarf and Slow-Growing Conifers came during the busiest weekend of the year at the U.S. National Arboretum. It was Mother's Day and the azaleas were in bloom. The Arboretum contains one of the largest collections of azaleas in the world, with over 60,000 plants. The blooming azaleas cover whole hillsides in a riot of color. People come from all over the world to witness it firsthand. It really is spectacular!

My husand and I drove from Ohio, staying overnight in West Virginia so we could get an early start Saturday morning. We were at the Arboretum when the gates opened, and started with a drive-through to see the roadside view of the azalea collection, then a walk-through, savoring and trying to absorb the beauty surrounding us.

We were so impressed with what we saw of the U.S. National Arboretum, that we spent the rest of the day visiting each of the separate collections and gardens. Each collection is quite wonderful, unique and an education in itself.

It was after we had visited most of the collections that we came to the Gotelli Collection. We were both amazed at the beauty and variety of plant material. It was hard to believe that an 'evergreen' (it was a while before the word 'conifer' came easily) could take so many forms, with so many variations in colors, textures and sizes. I had no idea that such variety existed. I was fascinated and wanted to know more.

When we returned home, I went to the library, and several book stores, in search of answers. I wanted to know more about those wonderful and unusual conifers. How, where and which ones could I get for our garden? And I wanted to know more about the Gotelli Collection - when? - who? - how? - why? My library search of book titles and subjects proved futile. A magazine article search resulted in a bit about the collection. But not nearly enough to satisfy my curiosity.

I visited my local garden center and tried to pick the brain of one of the owners, Jeff Andrey. He had graduated in horticulture and was quite knowledgeable about conifers. He brought out one of his text 'bibles' to show me photos of some of the cultivars I was questioning him about. It was Adrian Bloom's book, *Conifers for Your Garden.* After much persuasion and multiple promises, I was able to borrow this out-of-print book for the night. Then I was really hooked!

With the help of my local librarian and the inter-library loan system, I was able to borrow a copy of A. Bloom's book and many others (*see* Recommended Reading List). I checked out every book I could find with even a remote reference to conifers. The book stores did not have anything on their shelves. After searching through the available 'in print' catalogues, there was nothing I could order on dwarf conifers except one book for $75.00 (beyond my budget). I specifically requested several of the books I had found in the library, but they were all out of print; most of them had been published 20+ years previously. Now I wasn't just fascinated, I was frustrated. I am usually able to get several books on any subject I want to research. This was hard for me to accept.

Somewhere along this line, I contacted the U.S. National Arboretum to find out all I could on the Gotelli Collection. I was put in contact with Susan Martin, curator of the Gotelli Dwarf and Slow-Growing Conifer Collection. She confirmed that there was little publicly available on the Gotelli Collection, but she did provide me with copies of a few articles that had been written about it over the years. She suggested contacting the American Conifer Society.

Two things happened. First, I decided that if there wasn't a book about the Gotelli Collection, that there ought to be. If there wasn't anybody ready to write about it, then I would. My thinking was, and is, that the Gotelli Collection is so beautiful, special and unique, plus it's our National collection, actually a living museum, that there must be a lot of people out there who would want to know about it..... And if no one was going to write about it — and it needed to be written about — then I would write about it.

Second, I contacted the American Conifer Society ("ACS"), and found out that they were having their Annual Central Area Conifer Meeting right here in the Cleveland area just a few weeks from then. I attended, talked very little, and learned lots. I had come to the right place! I wanted to know about dwarf conifers, and these folks definitely knew about dwarf conifers!

I joined the ACS. I purchased several of their past Bulletins and read them cover-to-cover. The ACS Bulletins were full of information (much of it over my head), with lots of what I had been looking for plus lots I hadn't even known to look for. And there were a couple of articles authored by Susan Martin about the Gotelli Collection. Now I was starting to get somewhere!

That is how this book got started. . . Started, as in 'beginning', because that was just the beginning of an enormous project, and the beginning of my education!

The view from behind bed 1, looking north – A true study in contrasts!

The small shrub in the foreground/left is *Juniperus chinensis* 'Shimpaku', the widespreading, graceful mounding specimen in the center is *Cedrus deodara* 'Pendula, and the bright yellow, loosely-formed pyramid in the background/left is *Chamaecyparis pisifera* 'Gold Spangle'.

All three are from Gotelli's original collection, all over 35 years old. *J.c.* 'Shimpaku' is under 2' high and wide, *C.d.* 'Pendula' has a spread of 10-12' and is 5-6' high, and *C.p.* 'Gold Spangle' is close to 12' high and 7' wide. This is a good illustration of why you would want to know the growth rate of a specimen before you place it in your garden.

The box on a post to the right is the receptacle for maps at the entrance to The Gotelli Collection. We started from another direction, so didn't know they were available until we were almost through.

Overview

The order in this book is similar to my own experience, when we first visited the U.S. National Arboretum. First, the drive-through; an overview of our living museum. (Until we actually visited, I was only vaguely aware of the existence of a National Arboretum. Once I did visit, I wondered why I hadn't been aware of its beauty and resources much earlier in my life!) The second chapter is a walk-about down the paths of the Arboretum. The many group photos provided are just a small overview of the actual Collections. Many readers will want to see the actual plants for themselves, and some will be curious enough to want to see the many plants in the Collections that have not been included in this book. Bed numbers are referenced in most captions as a frame of reference for the readers who will visit the Arboretum.

The first two chapters show mature dwarf and unusual conifers in group settings, illustrating the wide choice of forms, textures, colors and sizes. Seeing these conifers grown in beautifully landscaped settings, grouped with complimentary companion plants, gives you lots of ideas for your own yard. It helps to see the sizes in relationship to each other. There are also many full-sized species conifers scattered throughout the Collection. In addition to the beauty and variety of the individual species, these full-sized conifers lend proportion to the mature dwarf conifers — Being able to compare a mature 12 to 15-foot 'dwarf' to its parent species of 120-150' mature height definitely helps lend perspective.

The third chapter is a short history of the Collections, showing some of the Gotelli conifers in their original home in New Jersey, the early days of the Collection moving to the Arboretum, and a short background on the Watnong Collection.

By the time I had finished my tour of the Conifer Collections, I was full of questions – Who was Gotelli, and why did he give his collection to the **public**? Why the name Watnong? Where could I get similar plants? How can I learn more? (Along in here somewhere, I learned how important it was to have the correct botanical name if I was at all serious about purchasing the right cultivar.) Assuming you will have similar questions, the fourth chapter provides a few answers, and tries to aim you in the right direction for more information.

Once you plant a few conifers, the question arises, 'How do I take care of them?' The descriptions chapter, along with the care & maintenance chapter, are to be used as continuing reference tools.

Botanical names have been used throughout this book because when you want a particular specimen, the only way to ensure that you have the right plant is to know the proper botanical name. Common plant names can vary by geographical regions, and often the same name is applied to entirely different plants. When you know the proper botanical name, you can avoid disappointment later.

Having written this book with the home owner in mind, the first reaction to the use of botanical names is probably, 'Why not use plain English?'. When you start acquiring dwarf and unusual conifers, you realize that this can be quite expensive – and when you're investing in these special conifers, you want to **know** you have purchased exactly what you had in mind. Knowing the proper botanical name is your insurance!

Before you even start – so you won't be totally frustrated with the exclusive use of the botanical names – cut out the two pages provided at the end of this book. They are duplicates of the common/ botanical names listed in the Glossary. Use them as book marks so they'll be handy when you need to refer to them—handier than flipping pages back and forth! (If you're borrowing this book, you have my permission to make a photocopy of those two pages.)

The view in early spring – standing on the hill at the west end of the Gotelli Collection, above bed 9.

Quick Reference for Common/Botanical Names

There are two pages at the end of this book provided specifically as an easy reference when you need it. They are duplicates of the cross-referenced Common–Botanical names from the Glossary. If this is your own book, cut them out, fold them down the middle, then use them as book-marks! If you're using a friend's book, or if this is from the library, take a photocopy of those two pages–you have my permission–then you'll have your own easy reference.

Driving Tour

The U.S. National Arboretum's
Dwarf Conifers

Begin your driving tour after a short stop at the Arboretum's Administration Building. (You'll enjoy the trip more if you stop for a map and brochures.) If you come in from the greenhouse end of the main parking lot (the few spots in front are usually full), there are steps leading to the terrace area behind the administration building. You'll enjoy this approach.

On the following page, you will see the Court of Honor, the terrace where the Arboretum's introductions are displayed, and where I gathered a grouping of container plantings. They include a sampling of a few plants from the Arboretum's Elite Introduction program.

On the way to The Gotelli Collection of Dwarf & Slow-Growing Conifers and The Watnong Collection, you pass by a few exhibits you'll want to come back to later. Your 'drive-through' of the Gotelli and Watnong Collections takes you along Conifer Road, around the outskirts of the Collections. You will be amazed at the variety in size, form, foliage and color among the conifers. Sizes range from towering giants to knee-high miniatures, with many examples of everything in between.

The drive-through should whet your appetite for more! The next chapter, you stop for a walk-about, getting a closer look as you meander through the many beds and groupings in both Collections.

above: This terrace, the Court of Honor, is the display area for the Arboretum's introductions. It is to the left and behind the Arboretum's Administration Building. As you approach the front of the Building, follow the path on the left. In the distance, to the right, is *Viburnum plicatum f. tomentosum* 'Shasta', one of my favorite shrubs.

below: Listing the plants in containers, starting on the left with the group of three – *left/back: Hydrangea macrophylla* 'Nigra'; *left/front: Ajania pacifica* 'Silver and Gold'; *left/middle: Ilex crenata* 'Sky Pencil'; *center: Chamaecyparis obtusa* 'Nana Aurea' (from the original Gotelli Collection); *right: Deutzia gracilis* 'Nikko'; *Euonymus japonica* 'Green Spire'; *right/front: Juniperus conferta* 'Blue Lagoon'; *Deutzia gracilis* 'Nikko'; *Miscanthus sinensis* 'Morning Light'; and the 2 spires in *back: Ilex crenata* 'Sky Pencil'.

above: The striking form of *Pinus thunbergiana* at the entrance to the Arboretum's Administration Building conveys a strong design statement that is in perfect harmony with the building. It is equally as striking whether you are entering or leaving the building. This *Pinus thunbergiana* is an excellent visual illustration of an outstanding specimen plant – outstanding from every angle. This particular specimen is pruned each spring during the candling stage, to enhance its structure and control its overall growth. Chapter 6 details this particular method of pruning pines.

Most people working inside this beautiful building would rather be outside working. The walls of windows make you feel like you're a part of the outdoors. A wonderful working environment… the next best thing to being there!

The bottom/left corner in the above/left photo, there is just a glimpse of the reflecting pool, which is almost a third of an acre in size, and surrounds the auditorium wing on three sides. You can view the extensive collection of aquatic plants in this pool from broad walkways and the terrace to the east, which is situated between the Administration Building and the The National Bonsai and Penjing Museum.

opposite page/bottom: Chamaecyparis obtusa 'Nana Aurea', from Gotelli's original collection, has been grown as a container plant since it was donated to the Arboretum in 1962. Placed beside it are specimens from the Arboretum's Elite Plant Introductions, all of which make excellent companion plants for dwarf conifers. (More information about these plants in Chapter 4 - Companion Plants.)

above: The Ellen Gordon Allen Garden, which includes this terraced area, is the transition garden at the entrance to the Japanese Pavilion and Stroll Garden; which in turn leads to other areas within the National Bonsai and Penjing Museum.

above/center: The artful specimen near the stairs is *Pinus thunbergiana*. Compare it with the specimen at the Administration Building entrance, previous page. Irregular branching is typical of the species, so each specimen develops a unique form.

The Formal Knot Garden, one of three main sections in The National Herb Garden. (Description – opposite page)

THE KNOT GARDEN

The formal knot expresses the traditional elegance of garden design which originated in Europe during the 16th century. Knot garden designs are geometrically patterned on a level site with plants arranged so they may be pruned to follow a pattern upon the ground.

This garden is a contemporary interpretation of the traditional knot garden. Dwarf evergreens, rather than herbs, have been used for improved uniformity and lower maintenance. The higher level of the reception area allows the knot to be viewed from above. Crushed brick is used in open spaces to emphasize intricate patterns forming the knot.

The National Capitol Columns are quite a majestic sight! I caught this view really early in the morning, as the sun was just rising, highlighting its stately appearance.

National Capitol Columns

The columns originally formed the east portico of the United States Capitol Building. In 1958 they were dismantled to make way for a new marble clad addition. They remained in storage for over 25 years before they were moved to the Arboretum, and, through the fund raising efforts of FONA, were dedicated in June 1990 as the **Capitol Columns at the Arboretum.** Quoting from the *History of the National Capitol Columns*, ". . .Corinthian Columns. . .were designed in ancient Rome, refined by the Italian Renaissance and brought to America in an English book." This is one of the many areas of special interest you will want to come back to so you can appreciate the full beauty, and in this case, the history involved.

The National Bonsai and Penjing Museum

The National Bonsai and Penjing Museum is a huge complex which includes the Japanese Pavilion and Stroll Garden, the North American Pavilion, and the Harua Kaneshiro Tropical Conservatory. The latest additions are the International and Chinese Pavilions.

Allow a full day for your visit – you will need plenty of time to absorb the amazing beauty displayed here. Quoting the U.S. Consulate in Hong Kong, "…the ultimate expressions of a form in which art, science, botany, gardening, and cultural traditions all intercross and intermix…"

The National Herb Garden

There are three major sections of the 2½-acre Herb Garden – the Knot Garden, the Historic or Old Rose Garden, and the series of 10 Specialty Gardens. It can easily take a full day to view these outstanding display gardens.

opposite page/bottom: Pictured is the view from the reception area terrace of the Herb Garden. Note the effective use of conifers with dramatic contrasts in color, form and texture – The golden conifer with the fern-like foliage is *Thujopsis dolabrata* 'Nana', and the silver/blue conifer is *Juniperus squamata* 'Blue Star'. The green shrub in the center, *Ilex crenata* 'Piccolo' is surrounded by a cultivar of the perennial *stachys*, and the green shrub planted to form the contasting circles interlocking the dwarf conifers is *Ilex crenata* 'Rotunda'.

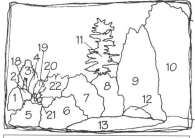

1 *Thuja plicata /Zebrina Mutant/*
2 *Picea pungens* 'Compacta'
3 *Abies firma*
4 *Picea pungens* 'Hoopsii'
5 *Thuja occidentalis* 'Filiformis'
6 *Picea abies* 'Pygmaea'
7 *Chamaecyparis obtusa* 'Sanderi'
8 *Platycladus orientalis* 'Aurea Nana'
9 *Thuja occidentalis* 'Semperaurea'
10 *Metasequoia glyptostroboides* 'National'
11 *Abies nephrolepis*
12 *Pinus sylvestris* 'Moseri'
13 *Juniperus conferta*
14 *Juniperus scopulorum* 'Alba'
15 *Buxus microphylla* 'Compacta'
16 *Juniperus communis*
17 *Chamaecyparis pisifera* 'Squarrosa Intermedia'
18 *Juniperus occidentalis* 'Sierra Silver' '
19 *Cedrus deodara*
20 *Taxus x media* 'Flushing'
21 *Thuja occidentalis* 'Emerald Green'
22 *Lagerstromia fauriei*
23 *Pinus mugo* 'Oregon Jade'

Just a quick stop... You need a closer look. There is an incredibly wide variety of plant material in this one vista. Interesting – Lively – Great contrasts – You know if you could possibly have a similar arrangement in your own yard, no one would ever be bored with the view!

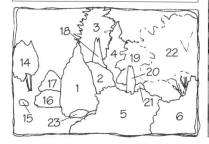

previous page – 1st week in May

Notice #5, *Thuja occidentalis* 'Filiformis'. To appreciate its dramatic color change each winter, *see* Descriptions – If you didn't know better, you would think it was dead. Knowing the change is natural, it's easier to appreciate its golden winter coloring (it helps to squint your eyes). It is a good choice, because its threadlike foliage and gently mounding, airy form add variety to the overall planting.

Four-Season Interest

"I only see three seasons!", you say…You will need to return in person to see the fall display! This grouping is at the north end of the Gotelli Collection, north side of Conifer Road, across the road from the scene on the opposite page.

The seasonal changes are dramatic, with the star magnolia and the Japanese maple taking center stage. These conifers form an interesting but not competitive backdrop for the seasonal displays, plus they carry their weight well as backdrops for the interesting bare forms of the maple and magnolia in winter. The individual conifers' seasonal changes contribute nicely to the year-round interest of this grouping with their differences in color, foliage and form; and especially with the spring flush of new growth and displays of emerging and maturing cones.

all photos this page: front–Acer palmatum 'Mouin'; right–Magnolia stellata 'Royal Star'; close background–Chamaecyparis pisifera 'Nana Aurea'; far background/left to right–Picea glehnii; Picea abies cv.; Picea pungens cv.

above: This vista shows the winter form of three separate species of deciduous conifers; *Metasequoia glyptostroboides*, *Taxodium distichum*, and *Glyptostrobus lineatus*. On the left, with pointed crowns and upward reaching branches, three towering *Metasequoia glyptostroboides*. Next, the outline with the rounded crown and outward branches is *Taxodium distichum*. Moving to the right, the tall outline in the middle/right of this photo is *Glyptostrobus lineatus*, and immediately right, and in the distance, is a grouping of *Metasequoia glyptostroboides* 'National'(also page 1-6).

above:
Vibrant contrasts in color, form and texture!

1 *Cedrus deodara* 'Aurea'
2 *Cedrus atlantica* 'Fastigiata'
3 *Cornus officianalis*
4 *Picea abies* cv.
5 *Spirea bumalda* 'Lime Mound'
6 *Pinus flexilis* 'Pendula'
7 *Acer palmatum* 'Sherwood Flame'
8 *Picea pungens* 'Compacta'
9 *Chamaecyparis obtusa* 'Crippsii'
10 *Picea abies* cv.
11 *Juniperus scopulorum*

opposite page/bottom: Featured in this view are golden larch, yew and sequoia against a complementary backdrop of mixed deciduous trees. The three specimens in front – from the *left:* The outreaching branches sparkling with fresh lime-green, almost yellow spring foliage – *Pseudolarix amabilis;* the broad shrub in the middle – *Taxus x media* cv.; and the broad pyramid with silvery green foliage, named in honor of Hazel Smith of Watnong Nurseries – *Sequoiadendron giganteum* 'Hazel Smith'. (She and her husband, Don, were the benefactors of the Watnong Collection.)

Left photo Spring – Right photo Fall

right: The broad silvery tower is the same *Sequoiadendron giganteum* 'Hazel Smith' as the opposite page, shown in the fall, looking further up Conifer Road. The broad dark green shrub at her base is *Taxus x media* cv., and the small green mound in the center is *Larix decidua* 'Pendula'. (Notice the relatively small size of *Larix decidua* 'Pendula'.)

Further to the right, the early morning sun dances through the golden fall foliage of *Betula nigra* 'Heritage'. Seen here only as dark green outlines because of the early morning sun, there are three large specimens (about 8' tall) of *Chamaecyparis obtusa* 'Rigid Dwarf'. At the base of this grouping, and placed to give the impression of a body of shimmering water, is the ground cover *Juniperus conferta* 'Blue Lagoon'.

above: Winter reveals the beautiful structure *Acer palmatum* 'Ornatum'. Part of Gotelli's original collection, this maple measured about 3' x 3' when it was donated in 1962 – thirty-five years later, it is 5½' high by 7' wide. The winter skeleton of a Japanese maple is an outstanding feature in most any garden, and it becomes more interesting and beautiful with age. *above right: Cedrus deodara* 'Aurea' has a beautiful 'sun-touched' golden hue all year long, but it is truly outstanding in the spring when its lush new foliage first appears. *above left: Cedrus atlantica* 'Aurea' is quite a sight each spring with the combination of its sparkling new growth and the emerging male pollen cones blanketing all the lower branches.

Dwarf Japanese maples make excellent companion plants for dwarf conifers. Their new leaves are forming at the same time the spring growth emerges on the conifers, lending dramatic contrast in form. They add to the overall harmony in summer with their flowing form, then their brilliant fall coloring compliments surrounding conifers.

left: Main entrance to the Gotelli Collection, the path between beds 1 (*left*) and 6 (*center*). (Looking directly into bed 6, note the sign for The Gotelli Dwarf and Slow Growing Conifers.) To the left is a box for maps, along with a bench, so you can relax as you study the map.

From the left, the first gold pyramid is *Chamaecyparis pisifera* 'Gold Spangle'; moving right to bed 6, the relatively small pyramid is *Chamaecyparis pisifera* 'Squarrosa Intermedia'; the towering blue/green pyramid is *Cedrus atlantica* 'Fastigiata'; the golden pyramid *front/right* is *Chamaecyparis pisifera* 'Gold Spangle'; all from Gotelli's original collection.

above: Referred to as 'Best of Beds' – The best cultivars available at local nurseries in 1978-79 were planted to show the choices of dwarf and slow-growing conifers available locally.

1 *Cornus florida*
2 *Hamamelis* 'Jelena'
3 *Chamaecyparis obtusa* 'Nana Gracilis'
4 *Lagerstroemia* 'Lipan'
5 *Pinus densiflora* 'Umbraculifera'
6 *Juniperus sabina* 'Buffalo'
7 *Picea pungens* 'Montgomery'
8 *Pinus strobus* 'Nana'
9 *Picea glauca* 'Conica'
10 *Juniperus scopulorum* 'Gray Gleam'
11 *Cryptomeria japonica* 'Yoshino' f. Bergman
12a *Juniperus procumbens* 'Horizontalis'
12b *Juniperus procumbens* 'Nana'
13 *Pinus mugo*
14 *Chamaecyparis pisifera* 'Snow'
15 *Cornus mas*
16 *Pinus strobus* 'Winter Gold'

below: Best of Beds – This section of beds is situated on the east side of Conifer Road, directly across the street from the main entrance to the Gotelli Collection.

above: mid-March – north end of the Watnong Collection

1 *Cedrus atlantica*
2 *Pinus cembra* 'Pygmaea'
3 *Pinus leucodermis* 'Compact Gem'
4 *Cedrus atlantica* 'Aurea'
5 *Pinus nigra* 'Hornibrookiana'
6 *Pinus cembra* 'Compacta Glauca'
7 *Cedrus atlantica* 'Fastigiata'
8 *Pinus sylvestris* 'Nana Compacta'
9 *Cedrus libani* var. *stenocoma*
10 *Cotinus* 'Velvet Cloak'

These two pages take you into the Watnong Collection, adjacent to the Gotelli Collection. As a frame of reference, note the Gotelli grouping pictured at the top of page 1-10. If the frames were a bit wider in the photos on the opposite page (Watnong Collection), they would overlap the Gotelli grouping.

Are you getting the impression the skies are a more intense blue in the Watnong Collection? That perhaps the sun shines brighter on this side of the hill than on the Gotelli Collection's side? Part of the illusion is magnified by the layout of Watnong where many of the conifers are planted high on the hillside, and can be viewed from the road. So as you're looking up to see the selections, you see lots of sky along with them. And when its a beautiful, bright, clear day, that's a lot of blue… a perfect backdrop for the these conifers!

Walking through the Collection gives a completely different perspective from the road view, so allow plenty of time to fully appreciate this beautiful display.

opposite page/bottom: last week in April – This time of year its worth the walk because it takes a closer inspection to fully appreciate the sparkling fresh spring beauty of these conifer specimens.

above: mid-March – The outlined forms of the conifers are much more prominent against the bare decisuous woods. Numbers 3 & 4 above are the same as 9 & 10 on the opposite page.

1 *Cedrus atlantica* 'Fastigiata'
2 *Pinus sylvestris* 'Nana Compacta'
3 *Cedrus libani* var. *stenocoma*
4 *Cotinus* 'Velvet Cloak'
5 *Pinus flexilis* 'Glauca' (thumes var.)
6 *Cedrus deodara* 'Limelight'
7 *Pinus pumila* selections
8 *Pinus sylvestris* 'Hillside' (Creeper)
9 *Pinus sylvestris* 'Fastigiata'
10 *Picea abies* cv.
11 *Pinus sylvestris* 'Albyns'

below: Same scene as above – last week in April.

Conifers Coming of Age

above (late April), *below* (mid-March) *and bottom/opposite page* (early May): This *Pinus strobus* grouping is situated at the west end of the Watnong Collection. The seasonal changes make you aware of the year-round beauty – My favorite time is during the spring candling stage, when this whole Collection appears to be celebrating.

Pinus strobus Grouping
1 P.s. 'Brevifolia'	6 P.s. (species)
2 Prunus (weeping)	7 Continus
3 P.s. 'Ontario'	8 P.s. 'Seacrest'
4 P.s. 'Brevifolia'	9 P.s. 'Brevifolia'
5 P.s. 'Laird's Broom'	10 P.s. 'Torulosa'

above: mid-March – Looking into the western end of the Watnong Collection. The variety of forms and relative sizes are easily distinguished in this late winter scene.

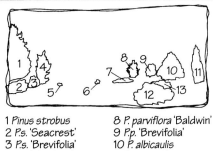

1 Pinus strobus
2 P.s. 'Seacrest'
3 P.s. 'Brevifolia'
4 P.s. 'Torulosa'
5 P.s. 'Ontario'
6 P.s. 'Hillside Gem'
7 P. resinosa 'Don Smith'
8 P. parviflora 'Baldwin'
9 P.p. 'Brevifolia'
10 P. albicaulis
11 Cedrus atlantica
     'Fastigiata'
12 P. strobus 'Brevifolia'
13 P.s. 'Macopin'

Pinus strobus Grouping
1 P.s. 'Brevifolia'
2 P.s. 'Ontario'
3 P.s. 'Laird's Broom'
4 P.s. (species)
5 P.s. /Redfield seedling/
6 P.s. 'Merrimack'
7 Continus
8 P.s. 'Seacrest'
9 P.s. 'Brevifolia'
10 P.s. 'Torulosa'

below: Pinus strobus grouping showing the candling stage. Note the overlap – numbers 8, 9 and 10 below are the same specimens as numbers 2, 3, and 4 in the photo above.

above: mid-March – West end of the Watnong Collection. This panoramic view includes the scenes on pages 14 and 15. The combination of the bare deciduous woods and this wide perspective view help illustrate the forms and relative sizes of these specimens. Can you identify specimens above from the photos and keys on the previous two pages?

Bed numbers are referenced in many captions as a frame of reference for those who have an opportunity to visit the Arboretum.

Walking Tour

The Gotelli & Watnong Conifer Collections

2

Catching glimpses of the interior of the Gotelli and Watnong Collections on your 'drive-thru,' your next step is, "I've got to see this – up close & personal." As you compare the mature sizes of the plants in the Collections, take note of the contrasting forms, foliage and colors. Notice how some cultivars stand out more than others, demanding center stage. Also note how some help to accentuate surrounding plant(s), while others complement, though both can add to the overall harmony of a particular planting. You'll discover which selections would soon outgrow their welcome if not given enough space, and which ones might be better with companion plants to empasize their diminutive size.

Not all the plants in the Collection are from Gotelli's original garden. Although there are over 300 of the original plants still 'maturing', this is not a stagnant collection. Susan Martin says they are always adding new material into it to keep up with the new cultivars. Quite a few of my favorites have been added within the last 10-15 years, and you may find the same is true for you.

Be sure to keep looking back! Not because you need to watch for someone, but because you need to turn around so you can fully appreciate the changing compositions as your perspective changes. You multiply the possibilities to compare the relative sizes, colors and forms, and how they highlight and/or harmonize in different settings.

below: Same scene as *above* & *right*, except I'm standing behind *Picea pungens* 'Compacta' & *Pinus mugo* /selection/ in bed 1, looking NW towards bed 3. The taller trees in the middle of the photo are also in the photo at the *top* of the next page. Can you identify which ones they are by their shape & coloring?

1 *Chamaecyparis pisifera* 'Gold Spangle'
2 *Viburnum tomentosum* 'Mt. Fuji'
3 *Picea pungens* 'Compacta'
4 *Pinus mugo* /selection/
5 *Sedum* 'Autumn Joy'
6 *Juniperus horizontalis* /selection/
7 *Chamaecyparis obtusa* 'Verdonii'
8 *Thuja occidentalis* 'Hetz Midget'
9 *Picea bicolor* 'Howell's Dwarf'

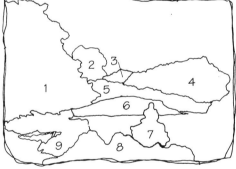

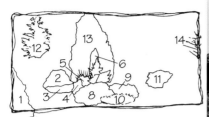

1 *Chamaecyparis pisifera* 'Gold Spangle'
2 *Cryptomeia japonica* 'Globosa Nana'
3 *Picea abies* 'Prostrata'
4 *Chamaecyparis obtusa* 'Verdonii'
5 *Molina caerulea subsp. altissima*
   'Karl Foerster'
6 *Juniperus communis* 'Pencil Point'
7 *Pinus parviflora* 'Koko-no-e'
8 *Picea bicolor* 'Howell's Dwarf'
9 *Thuja occidentalis* 'Hetz Midget'
10 *Iris*
11 *Picea pungens* 'Hunnewelliana'
12 *Cedrus libani* subsp. *stenocoma*
13 *Chamaecyparis obtusa* 'Crippsii'
14 *Pseudolarix amabilis*

far right photo:
1 *Cedrus deodara* 'Repandens'
2 *Chamaecyparis pisifera* 'Filifera'
3 *Picea abies* cv.
4 *Spiraea japonica* 'Alpina'
5 *Juniperus procumbens* 'Nana'
6 *Tsuga canadensis* 'Prostrata'

When you visit in person—turn around often—the scenes can appear completely different.

The lower four photos, taken at the intersections of beds 1, 2, 3, and 4, are all scenes that can be viewed from the same spot, merely by turning in different directions (and by visiting during different seasons…).
Cedrus libani subsp. *stenocoma* is the wispy branch fracturing the light in the upper left of the winter scene as we look back towards the entrance sign. It is seen from another direction in the top photo, #12, as you enter the Gotelli Collection.

Looking up the hill to the gazebo (*continuing up same path as photo directly above gazebo*), lightly covered with snow—though beautiful—does not give you quite the same feeling you would experience on a warm summer day, seeking a place of respite!

Conifers Coming of Age

left: Coming down the hill behind the Gotelli Collection from the western end, following this path takes you to the gazebo at the top of a clearing above beds 1 & 2. The spring display of azaleas in this area of the Collection rival the beauty of the main collections on Azalea Road.

left: same scene as above, early March, with the morning sun highlighting the grove. My friend, Linda Davis, gives proportion to the surroundings. There are very few dwarf conifers in this part of the Collection!

As you come down the slope from the gazebo, dwarf hemlocks are on both sides of the clearing, including one of my very favorites, *Tsuga canadensis* 'Cole's Prostrate'. It is easily missed, so be sure to look for it. It is over 35 years old, has a spread of about 3 x 4 feet, yet is hardly a foot tall. Its exposed branches give it an ancient, artistic look, and the gently cascading foliage is especially beautiful in early spring with the new growth highlighting all the tips – All the more beautiful if you can see it with the morning sunbeams streaking through the surrounding woods!

1 *Thuja occidentalis* 'Sunkist'
2 *Picea glehnii*
3 *Stewartia pseudocamellia*
4 *Picea orientalis* 'Gowdy'
5 *Pinus sylvestris* 'Beuvronensis'
6 *Cryptomeria japonica* 'Elegans Nana'
7 *Picea abies* 'Acrocona'

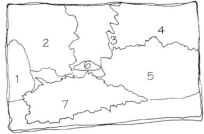

This is beautiful! Each time I look at one of these sunset photos, I can hear my friend (and assistant), Linda Davis, saying, "Hurry up, it's past closing time – we'll be locked in!" …and me, trying to get "just one more shot…" *Picea pungens* 'Compacta' is the star in both of these photos. Sunset and bright fall colors serve as a backdrop, outlining the wide, rounded symetrical form. The skirt surrounding this beautiful old cultivar is thick and lush…a wonderful specimen!

below: A light sprinkling of snow brightens the planting on an otherwise rather dark, dreary winter day.

below right: View the same scene with spring's fresh growth gracing the foliage tips, and a few whispy clouds drifting along in an intense blue sky.

above: Speaking of lush – framing *Picea pungens* 'Compacta', far left, *Picea abies* cv. is giving its most beautiful show of the year. The fresh, lemony new growth of spring stands out against the darker green of mature foliage, highlighting the tips of the long, draping branchlets covering its pointed, upward swooping branches. The overall effect is one of dense, lush, sparkling foliage. (This specimen has a witches' broom in it. *See* Descriptions)

1 *Cedrus libani* subsp. *stenocoma*
2 *Berberis verruculosa*
3 *Juniperus x media* 'Plumosa Aurea'
4 *Miscanthus sinensis* 'Variegatus'
5 *Juniperus procumbens* 'Nana'

Conifers Coming of Age

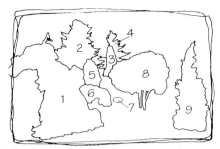

1 *Cedrus deodara* 'Pendula' 6 *Picea abies* 'Parsonii'
2 *Abies firma* 7 *Thuja plicata* 'Pygmaea'
3 *Picea pungens* 'Hoopsii' 8 *Pinus nigra* 'Globosa'
4 *Abies firma* 9 *Cupressus glabra*
5 *Tilia tomentosa* (Linden) 'Blue Ice'

left: The brilliant coloring of both plants is intensified by the contrast of the lime green of *Acer palmatum* 'Asahi-zuru' placed behind the clear blue of *Cupressus glabra* 'Blue Ice'. Their contrasting foliage and form further enhance this setting.

left: Standing in almost the same spot as the top photo, looking east on a fall afternoon: The contrasting golden foliage of the Heritage birch accentuates the large, dark silhouette of *Picea orientalis* 'Gowdy' (to the right of *Cupressus glabra* 'Blue Ice'). *Pinus sylvestris* 'Beuvronensis' appears as a gentle mounded form at the base of *P.o.* 'Gowdy'. To the left of *C.g.* 'Blue Ice', note how the yellow tips highlight the outline of *Thuja occidentalis* 'Sunkist'.

below: The brilliant splash of gold in the background is *Juniperus x media* 'Plumosa Aurea'. There are several plants of this cultivar throughout the Collection, providing highlights from many vantage points.

1 *Thujopsis dolabrata* var. *hondai*
2 *Juniperus chinensis* 'Sheppardii'
3 *Abies firma*
4 *Panicum virgatum* 'Rotstrahlbusch'
5 *Juniperus horizontalis*
6 *Picea abies* 'Repens'
7 *Chamaecyparis pisifera* 'Pygmaea'
8 *Spiraea nipponica*
9 *Thuja occidentalis* 'Hudsonica'
10 *Cedrus libani* 'Aurea Prostrata'
11 *Picea abies* 'Tabuliformis'
12 *Pinus mugo*
13 *Chamaecyparis pisifera*
   'Squarrosa Intermedia'

Cedrus deodara 'Aurea' takes center stage on this fall afternoon. In the distance, (across the road) the silver foliage and symmetrical forms of *Picea pungens* 'Royali' (*left*) and *Sequoiadendron giganteum* 'Hazel Smith' (*right*) stand out against the backdrop of golden fall colors. Not particularly noticable now, but a few weeks later, late fall – almost into winter – the foliage of *Pseudolarix amabilis* (*between P.p.* 'Royali' *and S.g.* 'Hazel Smith') turns a beautiful golden yellow before it looses its foliage. One of the first deciduous trees to break dormancy in spring, *Pseudolarix amabilis* takes the limelight for a short time each spring when its delicate, lime green foliage stands out against its stark, dark brown twiggy branches.

1 *Cotoneaster adpressa* var. *praecox*
2 *Picea abies* 'Gregoryana Parsonii'
3 *Picea abies* 'Repens'
4 *Juniperus scopulorum* 'Grey Gleam'
5 *Picea pungens* 'Iseli Foxtail'
6 *Picea abies* 'Ohlendorfii'
7 *Picea orientalis* 'Aurea Compacta'
8 *Picea abies* 'Pseudo prostrata'
9 *Picea abies* 'Oldhamiana'

10 *Juniperus scopulorum* 'Pathfinder'
11 *Pseudolarix amabilis*
12 *Picea abies* 'Capitata'
13 *Cedrus atlantica* 'Fastigiata'
14 *Pinus strobus* 'Nana'
15 *Chamaecyparis obtusa* 'Crippsii'

16 *Picea abies* cv. Hystric
17 *Pinus sylvestris* 'Viridis Compacta'
18 *Picea abies* 'Humilis'
19 *Juniperus horizontalis*
20 *Picea abies* 'Pendula'
21 *Lagerstroemia* x 'Tuskegee'

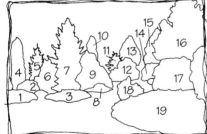

below left: early spring right: late summer

The fresh, new growth of spring almost shouts with vibrancy. A few months later, the muted colors of summer's mature foliage impart a more relaxed, mellow feeling.

This viewpoint allows you to see a wide variety of cultivars at once, where you can see (aided by the time lapse in these photos) that some specimens' colors change dramatically with the seasons, while others change very little.

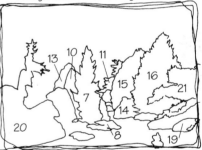

photo by Susan Martin

Conifers Coming of Age

From the *left: Picea omorika* 'Pendula', you'll often see its odd little branchlet drooping out ('standing out' doesn't quite apply with this very pendulous specimen.) near the top, *Picea pungens* 'Glauca Pendula', unique beyond description, and *Tsuga canadensis* 'Brandley', lush and full, especially impressive with its new spring growth.

When you're walking in the western and northern areas of the Collection, you will spot these three extraordinary specimens in many different scenes as your viewpoint changes.

You are sure to see many 'must-have's' as you meander through the many display beds. I've only presented a sampling of the views. You will need to see the Arboretum for yourself to realize how amazingly beautiful everything is — An ongoing, ever-changing, living display.

As you stroll through these pages, take note of the companion plantings, and see which ones might help highlight favorite conifers in your own garden.

above: Spring, bed 32 – *below:* October, bed 32

The tight vertical growth of *Pinus sylvestris* 'Spaan's Slow Column' is emphasized with its spring green candles shooting straight upward in the spring photo. It doesn't stand out nearly as much in the fall, when its coloring is more muted. A sense of harmony in this grouping is provided by the blues in the mounding specimens, the blue grass, and the splashes of blue in the ground covering. And the gently mounding shapes are set off nicely by surrounding gravel, stone outcroppings, and colorful larger cultivars in the background.

This is an example where new cultivars are planted among the original Gotelli specimens.

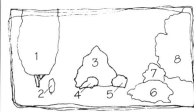

1 *Juniperus occidentalis* 'Glauca'
2 *Pinus sylvestris* 'Spaan's Slow Column'
3 *Chamaecyparis pisifera* 'Squarrosa Intermedia'
4 *Picea pungens* 'Procumbens'
5 *P. orientalis* 'Repens'
6 *Cedrus deodara* 'Devinely Blue'
7 *C.p.* 'Squarrosa Intermedia'
8 *C. obtusa* 'Tetragona Aurea'

above: first week in May (a cold, overcast sort of day). Notice how the deciduous trees and shrubs have filled in.
right: last week in April, everything is just starting to sparkle with new Spring growth.

below: Pinus bungeana is extremely slow-growing when young – and 'young' for this specimen can mean the first 10 to 20 years. With slow-growing conifers, the yearly growth rate along with the approximate size in ten years is the information you need in order your plan your landscape.

The *Pinus bungeana* below is a good example: It was started from seed in 1967. This specimen was moved to this bed about ten years ago, which probably slowed its already slow growth even more for the first year or so after it was moved. Though close to 30 years old, this plant is only 10-12 feet tall. It can take fifty years for this specimen to reach its ultimate height of 50 feet. Using the usual method of dividing the ultimate height by the number of years to reach UH (50 feet divided by 50 years equals 1 foot per year), the expected height for this specimen would be 10' in 10 years, 20' in 20 years, 30' in 30 years, etc. For this specimen especially, the calculations would result in the wrong expectations. Check out the 'general rule', especially if placement and growth rate are important factors.

below/center: Pinus bungeana has the morning light sparkling through, accentuating its airy form. The ground-hugging mat is *Juniperus horizontalis* 'Douglasii', left of *P.b.,* the medium-sized specimen is *Juniperus davurica* 'Expansa Variegata', *Tsuga canadensis* 'Bennett' is behind *J.d.,* and *Cornus kousa* var. *chinensis* is the light winter outline form on the left—altogether a really nice grouping!

above: The same scene as below – a couple weeks later – with the fresh new spring growth sparkling everywhere. This view is from behind bed 9, looking towards the pond. This reference is only significant if you visit the Arboretum, but when you do, you may want to seek out this same vista. It is breathtaking, and it changes with each season – enjoy!

left: In late April, you can usually catch the magnolias in bloom – taking center stage for just a short time in early spring. April isn't when you can count on the skies being clear or the sun shining bright each day, but you can count on lots of color and contrasts from the early blooming shrubs tucked in amongst the conifer plantings, and the coloring of the conifers becoming more intense as the weather warms and new growth emerges.

Looking west into the horizon, *Cedrus atlantica* 'Glauca' can easily be spotted with its silver-blue foliage and broad, symmetrical form. Its massive size is more noticeable as you come closer to it.

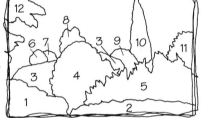

1 *Juniperus procumbens* 'Nana' – growing into:
2 *Juniperus horizontalis* 'Douglasii'
3 *Tsuga canadensis* 'Kelsey's Weeping'
4 *Tsuga canadensis* 'Jervis'
5 *Juniperus x media* 'Plumosa Aurea'
6 *Chamaecyparis pisifera* 'Squarrosa Intermedia'
7 *Picea pungens* 'Compacta'
8 *Chamaecyparis obtusa* 'Tetragona Aurea'
9 *Tsuga canadensis* 'Herman Hesse'
10 *Juniperus occidentalis* 'Glauca'
11 *Tsuga canadensis* 'Jervis'
12 *Tilia tomentosa* (Linden)

1 *Chamaecyparis obtusa* 'Spiralis'
2 *Chamaecyparis obtusa* 'Nana Lutea'
3 *Chamaecyparis obtusa* 'Tempelhof'
4 *Pinus cembra*
5 *Chamaecyparis obtusa* 'Reis Dwarf'
6 *Deutzia gacillis* 'Nikko'
7 *Picea abies* 'Tabuliformis'
8 *Chamaecyparis obtusa* 'Chilworth'

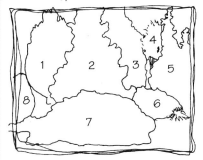

left: A few of the variations in form, color, and foliage available within the *Chamaecyparis obtusa* cultivars – with well over 100 named cultivars to choose from.

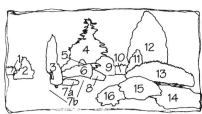

1 *Pinus strobus* 'Winter Gold'
2 *Picea orientalis* 'Nana'
3 *Juniperus scopulorum* 'Grey Gleam'
4 *Cedrus deodara* 'Aurea'
5 *Picea glauca* 'Conica'
6 *Pinus strobus* 'Nana'
7a *P. mugo*
7b *J. procumbens* 'Nana'
8 *Picea pungens* 'Montgomery'
9 *Chamaecyparis pisifera* 'Plumosa Compressa'
10 *Cedrus deodara* 'Pendula'
11 *Chamaecyparis pisifera* 'Gold Spangle'
12 *Cedrus atlantica* 'Fastigiata'
13 *Pinus densiflora* 'Umbraculifera'
14 *J. sabina* 'Broadmoor'
15 *Picea abies* 'Nidiformis'
16 *J. s.* 'Broadmoor'

The two towering giants in this grouping are *Abies firma*–*left*, *Picea pungens* 'Hoopsii'–*center*. *Chamaecyparis pisifera* 'Squarrosa Intermedia' is the larger mounded form–*left*, *Ilex crenata* 'Sky Pencil' is the small vertical statement–*right*, with the mat-forming ground cover *Juniperus horizontalis* 'Bar Harbor'–*front center*, and *Chamaecyparis pisifera* 'Monstrosa' is the rounded form–*right*.

C. p. 'Monstrosa' looks neat and tidy, so it must have just received its maintenance clipping… without regular clipping of its long shoots of 'rank' growth, this specimen would be enormous. It has an unusaul combination of dark green adult foliage and compact, almost blue, juvenile foliage; and each form separate sections on the plant. Very interesting!

below, center: *Pinus strobus* 'Winter Gold' makes s a wonderful specimen plant. Its bright winter color is a pleasant sight on a dreary day, and on a sunny day, with sun behind it, it glows like a beacon. When planted with symetrically formed and dark green specimens, its bright color and loose, open form make a pleasant contrast.

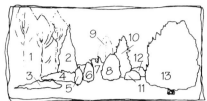

1 *Metasequoia glyptostroboides* 'National'
2 *Juniperus x media* 'Fairview'
3 *Picea pungens* 'Glauca Prostrata'
4 *Juniperus virginiana* 'Kosteri'
5 *Pinus sylvestris* 'Sentinal'
6 *Chamaecyparis thyoides* 'Andelyensis'
7 *Juniperus virginiana* 'Grey Owl'
8 *Platycladus orientalis* 'Aurea Nana'
9 *Taxodium distichum*
10 *Abies pinsapo* 'Glauca'
11 *Pinus sylvestris* 'Riverside Gem'
12 *Picea pungens* 'Compacta'
13 *Pinus flexilis* 'Vanderwolf's Pyramid'

above: mid-March, facing east, back to bed 21. You can see one of the identifying differences between *Metasequoia glyptostroboides* and *Taxodium distichum*. *M.g.* 'National' (#3), pointed crown and upward pointing branches (also true of species) – *T.d.* (#9) rounded crown and outward reaching branches.

The difference seasons can place a whole new perspective on the same scene. The photos on these two pages were taken from different positions in the same area; the northwestern part of the collection, near bed 35. Note where *Pinus sylvestris* 'Riverside Gem' and *Platycladus orientalis* 'Aurea Nana' appear in each photo.

below: mid October, looking north into bed 35, background far left is bed 36.

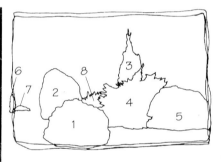

Key for drawings above & below:

1 *Pinus sylvestris* 'Riverside Gem'
2 *Platycladus orientalis* 'Aurea Nana'
3 *Juniperus x media* 'Fairview'
4 *Juniperus virginiana* 'Grey Owl'
5 *Pinus sylvestris* 'Beuvronensis'
6 *Pinus sylvestris* 'Sentinal'
7 *Picea pungens* 'Glauca Prostrata'
8 *Miscanthus sinensis* 'Condensatus'
9 *Pinus sylvestris* 'Globosa Viridis'
10 *Pinus flexilis* 'Vanderwolf's Pyramid'
11 *Chamaecyparis pisifera* 'Golden Mop'

below: mid June, bed 35 on the right, looking west towards bed 21.

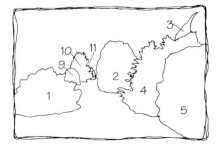

Cedrus libani 'Nana', shown on the left in both photos, matures into a good-sized specimen.
Picea omorika 'Pendula' is easy to pick out in a crowd! We're looking directly west in this
photo.

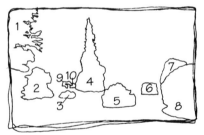

1 Abies pinsapo 'Glauca'
2 Cedrus libani 'Nana'
3 Thuja occidentalis 'Globosa Rheindiana'
4 Picea omorika 'Pendula'
5 Pinus sylvestris 'Riverside Gem'
6 Pinus sylvestris 'Globosa Viridis'
7 Platycladus orientalis 'Aurea Nana'
8 Pinus sylvestris 'Beuvronensis'
9 Picea pungens 'Glauca Pendula'
10 Juniperus x media 'Plumosa Aurea'

A few steps one way or another, turning around, visiting during different seasons, or coming a year later during the same season, the scene changes, giving you a whole different perspective of the plantings. Many times I noticed a plant for the first time, sure it hadn't been there the last time I was in that particular spot!

These two photos were both taken in May, the one above in 1994, and below in 1995. Noting the beautiful blue skies and fresh new foliage — May is a great time to visit!

Cedrus libani 'Nana' on the left, looking north, facing Platycladus orientalis 'Aurea Nana' and Pinus sylvestris 'Beuvronensis', with Juniperus x media 'Grey Owl' between them, and Pinus sylvestris 'Riverside Gem' in the foreground.

1 *Juniperus horizontalis* 'Wiltonii'
2 *Juniperus communis* 'Gold Cone'
3 *Chamaecyparis pisifera*
    'Plumosa Aurea Compacta'
4 *X Cupressocyparis leylandii* 'Naylor's Blue'
5 *Sciadopitys verticillata*
6 *Chamaecyparis obtusa* 'Nana Gracilis'
7 *Taxus baccata* 'Fastigiata Robusta'
8 *Taxodium distichum*
9 *Pinus mugo* 'Mops'

1 *Tsuga canadensis* 'Jervis'
2 *Chamaecyparis obtusa* 'Nana Lutea'
3 *Tsuga canadensis* 'Kelseyii'
4 *Juniperus procumbens* 'Nana'
5 *Pinus wallichiana* 'Zebrinia'
6 *Tsuga canadensis* /selection/
7 *Chamaecyparis pisifera* 'Monstrosa'

above: Lots of information right here in one spot! Touching on a bit of it: – *Chamaecyparis* Pisifera 'Plumosa Aurea Compacta' has reverted so much that very little is left of the true cultivar. Cuttings will be taken from the 'true' portion, and this specimen will be replaced. – Bare of foliage against the vivid blue sky, *Taxodium distichum* is easy to identify by its rounded crown. – *Pinus mugo* 'Mops' is a start from Gotelli's original *P.m.* 'Mops' a few yards away, which is barely 3' tall (a cultivar that stays within its bounds!) – *X Cupressocyparis leylandii* 'Naylor's Blue' is quite common. Its symmetrical form and graceful, full foliage contribute to its popularity.

below: Pinus wallichiana 'Zebrinia' is an outstanding cultivar. If you have the space for a full-sized specimen, its graceful habit and bright coloring make it a beautiful addition to the landscape. This specimen died in 1994, but this glimpse might give you ideas for its placement.

above: Pinus strobus 'Macopin' is the wide, layered cultivar–left, Pinus strobus 'Ontario' is the small mound–center background, and Pinus strobus 'Nana', rather larger than what you'd expect of a 'Nana'–right.

below, left page: The bed in the foreground is an especially pleasant combination of plant material.

Although it's a help to see what the mature sizes look like, when you see a setting that would be ideal to duplicate – keep in mind that it took 35 years to accomplish this flowing harmony. These are slow-growing cultivars, so planning should be in terms of ten-year spans of growth, rather than expecting dramatic changes in a few short years.

'**Early April in the Park**' – Beautiful, isn't it! Clear blue skies in April might be expecting too much... and April showers might cause dropping of the flowers. So when you know the trees are covered with blossoms, enjoy them when you have the chance. If you wait for ideal weather, it may be too late.

These two scenes take you into the Watnong Pinetum, adjacent to the Gotelli Collection. It includes 57 cultivars of 16 species of pine. European cultivars are placed in the eastern end of the Pinetum, directly above the parking area, Asian cultivars–in the center, and cultivars native to the United States– the western end.

below: In the foreground is Pinus albicaulis, and center is Pinus koraiensis 'Glauca', with its broad pyramidal form outlined against the spring blossoms.

Conifers Coming of Age

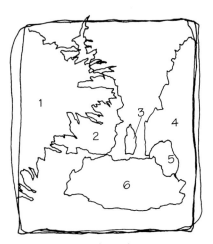

1 *Cedrus atlantica* 'Aurea'
2 *Cedrus libani* subsp. *stenacoma*
3 *Pinus sylvestris* 'Fastigiata'
4 *Cedrus atlantica* 'Fastigiata'
5 *Pinus cembra* 'Compacta Glauca'
6 *Pinus nigra* 'Hornibrookiana'

right: An example of contrasts in forms and textures, and the hormonious feeling conveyed in this type of composition. (The blue sky helps!)

opposite page and below: The mounded form on the left is *Pinus thunbergiana* 'Yatsubusa', and the upward swooping form is *Pinus thunbergiana*/Corticosa Group (interpretation – its member of a group with characteristic corkbark). I particularly enjoy the drama of the three different seasons, especially when seen from this perspective. When viewed from this distance, the conifers appear consistant; but they blend, contrast and take center stage in time with the seasonal changes provided by their deciduous backdrop.

above: A wonderful winter study of color and form.

Center, the irregular zig zag form and brilliant gold of *Pinus sylvestris* 'Aurea' is a pleasing contrast to the icy blue rounded form behind – *Picea pungens* 'Compacta'. The ground-hugging form and plum-colored winter foliage of *Juniperus horizontalis* 'Bar Harbor' compliments both the blue-toned foliage of *Picea glauca* 'Wild Acres' on the left, and the tight, mounding form of *Picea abies* 'Mucronata' on the right. The broad deciduous form revealing its characteristic up-reaching branches, outlined in the upper right, is *Metasequoia glyptostroboides* 'National'.

History

3

The Gotelli & Watnong Conifer Collections

Wm. T. Gotelli was described as "…an intense collector of unbridled enthusiasm…" He was aware of invaluable collections that had been disbursed when the owners died, and Gotelli did not want this to happen to his collection — He wanted it kept intact, in order to preserve its essential character. Sylvester 'Skip' March, former chief horticulturist at the Arboretum, is quoted as saying, "I must emphasize, that the Gotelli donation was not a case of a man of means erecting a monument to himself. It was, rather, a feeling of reciprocity between Mr. Gotelli and the Arboretum. Both parties wished to see the introduction of these plants into cultivation and the subsequent knowledge used to benefit horticulture."

Has your curiosity started running? Who was William T. Gotelli? What motivated him to contribute such a collection to the **public**? How long did it take him to collect all these plants? Where did he find them? What is the history behind the Watnong Collection? Are you still coming up with questions??? The next few pages should help.

Mr. Gotelli spent his childhood in Oregon, and later became a successful building contractor in the New York Metropolitan Area. Gardening had been his hobby since 1941, and as he read about conifers, his interest gradually focused on dwarf and slow-growing conifers. His search for 'little conifers' eventually took him to many countries around the world.

This was Mr. Gotelli's dining room view of his arboretum.

One view of the one and a half acres Mr. Gotelli devoted to growing dwarf and unusual conifers.

The Gotelli Arboretum

Mr. William T. Gotelli's personal arboretum was located at his home in South Orange, New Jersey, on 1½ acres, with the plants grown in gardens and beds surrounding his home. His garden was open and wasn't screened from the public, so a major part of his collection could be viewed from the street.

The plants for Mr. Gotelli's arboretum were collected during a 15 year period prior to 1960, and eventually contained over 800 varieties of conifers, 600 varieties of rhododendrons, and many Japanese maples. His collecting took him all over the world, doing business with over 250 nurseries in the U.S., Japan, Europe, New Zealand, Australia, and Canada. He estimated the final cost of assembling his conifers at about $500,000.

Mr. William T. Gotelli at the New York Flower Show – 1960

All photos on this page are courtesy of the USNA.

Their close proximity to the quarantine station in Glendale allowed the National Arboretum to watch over Mr. Gotelli's imported plants during the quarantine period. As the staff at the National Arboretum was exposed to the exotic conifers brought in by Mr. Gotelli, they began to develop an interest in this area. This budding interest was aided by Mr. Gotelli's donation of many specimens to the National Arboretum over the years.

Over the 15 years of gathering and importing the collection, a strong relationship developed between Mr. Gotelli and the staff at the National Arboretum. This long-standing relationship culminated in Mr. Gotelli's donation of the entire collection to the National Arboretum in 1962. At that time, he and his wife had decided to sell their home and move to another location, and it was important to Mr. Gotelli that the collection be perpetuated and improved for future generations. The moderate climate in the Washington, D.C. area was also a contributing factor, with its proven ability to grow conifers that thrive in the warmer southern regions of the U.S., as well as those that thrive in the cooler northern regions of the U.S.

above: A view of the rock garden area of Mr. Gotelli's arboretum.

I do wish I could provide you with a sketch and key to this interesting array of conifers! Isn't this a wonderful mixture of colors, forms, textures and sizes? The ultimate fine tuning of contrasts and complements! I am particularly impressed with the balance and brilliant coloring of the many blue cultivars. And the yellow pyramid in the back/center...outstanding color, and great contrast to its surroundings!

above: Another view of the same rock garden as *left*. This was probably taken from about where the yellow pyramid is in the photo on the left, looking back toward Mr. Gotelli's home.

A few specimens are shown in both photos. Can you find which ones they are? And if you can do that, can you match them to the mature specimens pictured in this book? If you <u>can</u> do that, please provide me with the information, and I will include a key with the next printing of this book.

right: I especially wanted to include this photo showing each of the specimens carefully balled and burlapped before the move to the Arboretum. I didn't see any photos of Mr. Gotelli's yard after the Collection was moved, but I can imagine it looked similar to photos I've seen of the moon – full of craters!

The actual move was done in a relatively short time. I wondered if it took place over a year's time or several months. Although it took many trips, the actual moving was done in a matter of several weeks.

Take special note of the thorough job that was done in the balling & burlapping of each specimen. It truly is a matter of life or death – whether or not a plant is properly balled and burlapped before being moved. The method is referenced in the Care and Maintenance chapter, but this is the only illustration provided.

All photos on this page are courtesy of the USNA.

Conifers Coming of Age

Cedrus atlantica 'Glauca' during the big move!

I had read accounts of this blue atlas cedar lifting the crane, but until I spoke with "Skip" March, I didn't have the whole 'scoop'. The Arboretum was using its own equipment to move the *Cedrus atlantica* 'Glauca': With the combined weight of the enormous tree and its eight foot root ball, the expected was reversed — the tree lifted the crane! A heavier crane was leased to complete the job, at a cost of $150.00 for the day. From then on, whenever anyone questioned "Skip" about what *C.a.* 'Glauca' was worth, he enjoyed replying, "Well, I know it is worth at least $150.00."

All photos on this page are courtesy of the USNA.

all photos above, left, page 3-1, and pages 3-6&7: **Cedrus atlantica** 'Glauca' – The largest tree in the Gotelli Collection. At the time it was moved, it measured 25 feet high by 15 feet wide, and the diameter of the root ball measured 8 feet. It was between 20-25 years old when Mr. Gotelli purchased it in 1955, and at that time it measured 8' wide by 10' high.

opposite page/top/left: Very little amending was done to the soil prior to planting the Gotelli Collection at the National Arboretum because this area already had a proven history of growing conifers. The collection of older specimens lies directly west, adjacent to the Gotelli Collection. There are quite a few unique, mature specimens among this older collection where many conifers were planted as early as 1942.

opposite page/bottom/left: To enjoy a journey through time, see pages 1-10 and then 2-12 (33 years later.) After you compare the towering, mature specimen of *Cedrus deodara* 'Aurea', you will understand why I asked Susan Martin if this was indeed the same specimen Mr. Gotelli referred to in his notes. It is. She speculated that at some point it must have developed a strong leader branch that completely dominated the spreading tendency. Although, she pointed out, the ends of the lower branches still tend to be pendulous, especially the branch tips.

above: A view looking west, of the clearing and preparation that took place prior to planting more of the Gotelli Collection. The background shows several beds where the planting is completed. At the horizon line, in the center, notice the outline of *Cedrus atlantica* 'Glauca' along with the outlines of a few specimens from the older collection of conifers.

above: Simulated rock croppings were placed throughout the Collection. The plant on the lower right is *Juniperus communis* 'Echiniformis'. Mr. Gotelli referred to this plant as one of the 'true dwarf conifers' – its annual growth rate is about ¼" per year. See this specimen 33 years later on page 5-21.

The pendulous, wide-spreading specimen on the slope behind the sign is *Cedrus deodara* 'Aurea'. Mr. Gotelli purchased this specimen in 1959 as *Cedrus deodara* 'Aurea Pendula', at which time it had a spread of 3'. He indicated in his notes to the Arboretum that it was 2' high by 8' wide 11/15/62, and that he had found it to be a fast grower, having doubled its size in a few years. He also noted it had the tendency to spread out, not up.

This is bed 1 as it appeared shortly after the initial planting of the Gotelli Collection. Note the placement of *Juniperus communis* 'Echiniformis' above the first rock outcropping, and *Cedrus atlantica* 'Glauca' – it appears past the bed, outlined against the horizon. Enjoy comparing with pages 2-2 and 2-3 – this same area 33 years later.

All photos on this page are courtesy of the USNA.
following pages: Cedrus atlantica 'Glauca' May - 1994

above: November –1963

Mr. Gotelli's friend and garden designer, John Jennings, provided the general layout for the beds, paths, and placement of larger specimens; and the actual planting and placement of the rest of the plants was done by the Arboretum. It wasn't only plants that were moved: The actual simulated rock used at Mr. Gotelli's arboretum was moved to the Arboretum and incorporated into the overall landscape.

left: The simulated rock croppings appear completely natural. During my many visits to the Arboretum, I've never actually tapped them to find out if they felt or sounded different – I had intended to once I learned they were simulated rock, but I never remembered to do it when I was there because they appear so natural.

above: June – 1965

Dr. Henry T. Skinner, Director of the Arboretum at that time, took an active part in the placement of the simulated rock outcroppings. It was everyone's intention that the whole area have a natural appearance, and, as it happened, Dr. Skinner was particularly well qualified for this task, having written a booklet on rock gardening while working on his Ph.D at Cornell University.

left: Notice the field lath house that was built to protect a Japanese maple while it becomes established. It was after viewing this photo that I started protecting my summer transplants by constructing temporary structures from pieces of prefabricated lattice. It made a major difference in my failure/success rate.

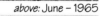

below: August – 1966   *above:* June – 1965

The Gotelli Collection was moved in summer, the most stressful season for the plants. Although there were not many fatalities, due to transplanting during the summer there were some losses. Extra precautions taken to prevent losses – large specimens were planted right away, while many smaller plants were kept in a lath house.

It was three years before planting of the Gotelli Collection was completed, and it took close to ten years before some specimens outgrew their allotted space. When the plants were donated, no one knew how large some of the specimens would eventually grow. It was after fifteen years that some dwarfs turned out to be not so dwarf, and some plants that reverted to normal size had to be removed.

When you grow dwarf conifers, it is important to watch for reversions which should be pruned out as soon as possible. The reverted foliage is much more vigorous than its dwarf counterpart, and if left to grow it soon dominates the specimen.

left: This photo shows how annuals were used to fill in open spaces between the conifers, and it appears that in some areas they overwhelmed the conifers. More recently, perennials, bulbs and shrubs have been used to compliment and enhance the dwarf, unusual and slow-growing conifers, rather than just to fill in spaces…

Turn back to page 1-10 for this scene, 1994 version.

All photos on this and opposite page are courtesy of the USNA.

1 *Pinus strobus* 'Pendula'
2 *Juniperus procumbens* 'Nana'
3 *Chamaecyparis obtusa* 'Pygmaea'
4 *C. obtusa* 'Intermedia'
5 *C. pisifera* 'Squarrosa Intermedia'
6 *gone*
7 *Thuja occidentalis* 'Globosa Rheindiana'
8 *Cedrus deodara* 'Pendula'

August – 1966

July – 1962

May – 1981
photo by Susan Martin

above: Pinus strobus 'Pendula' measured 8'H/12'W when it was first moved to the Arboretum. Mr. Gotelli acquired it in 1945 from George Ehrle. It measured 6'/H at that time.

This specimen (as you'll see on the next two pages) is over fifty years old! Its all right to be overly large, slightly lumpy and definitely pendulous – at the same time uniquely attractive – when you're **old**! A wonderful example of 'growing old gracefully'!

above: October – 1964 *Pinus strobus* 'Pendula' – It's not dying. Once you know its supposed to look like this, you can enjoy the bicolor effect! Each fall about 1/3 of its needles turn golden before being shed.
below: June – 1994 *Pinus strobus* 'Pendula'

The view above gives an unusual perspective! I am standing behind *Pinus strobus* 'Pendula', allowing its fall coloring and massive branches to frame my view. *Cupressus glabra* 'Blue Ice' shines like a beacon out in the bright sunshine. The contrasts are emphasized even more with my view of *C.g.* 'Blue Ice' next to the dark outline of *Chamaecyparis obtusa* 'Verdonii'. The combination of the two (*C.g.* 'Blue Ice'/ *C.o.* 'Verdonii') forms a nice contrast in color, texture of foliage, form and size.

After seeing this, I've incorporated a similar combination in my own garden. ...Now if I just had a huge, mature specimen of *Pinus strobus* 'Pendula', it would be perfect!

Don and Hazel Smith, donors of the Watnong Collection of Slow-Growing and Dwarf Pines.   photo courtesy of the USNA

There is an interesting story about this sign that provides insight into the Smiths' personalities: They were adament about the name of the Collection – It was to be 'Watnong'. They did not want it to be known as the 'Smith Collection'.

As circumstances would have it, the first sign installed at the Collection had 'Smith Collection...' imprinted on it. This original photo was taken at the dedication of the Collection, when the sign had 'Smith...' instead of 'Watnong...'.

Susan Martin allowed me to use this photo on the condition and understanding that I make **sure** the original photo would be modified so the sign read 'Watnong'. Because she was sure the Smiths would be mortified and 'turn over in their graves' if their photo was published showing the original sign (it was corrected and replaced very soon after this photo was taken).

The Watnong Collection

In 1979, Don and Hazel Smith donated a group of 60 pines from their private pinetum at the Watnong Nursery. Located on a little over an acre of land in Morris Plains, New Jersey, their nursery was situated on a downhill slope of "a little hill." They chose the name Watnong because of its Indian meaning, "little hill."

The idea for their Watnong Nursery was formulated in 1954, with the goal of finding and making available dwarf and slow-growing plants suitable to small properties. When Don retired from his position as public school superintendent in 1961, the Watnong Nurery was opened with 40 selections displayed on a wheelbarrow in their back yard. The nursery was the culmination of dwarf evergreens collected from arboretums and private gardens throughout the U.S. and Europe.

The Smiths specialized in plants that had not been formerly available to the public. They discovered, propagated and introduced dozens of plants, generously sharing their time and their plants. Sharing was charactaristic of the Smiths, who felt a plant should always be growing in at least two places so if one dies, they could always get one back.

In the 1960s and early 70s, the Smiths traveled the East Coast, giving lectures, and educating people about the usefulness of slow-growing and unusual plants. Within a decade, the Watnong Nursery had gained an international reputation for dwarf conifers and broad-leaved evergreens. It was in the late 70's that the Smiths began donating major portions of their collection to public arboretums.

The group of approximately 60 pines donated to the National Arboretum contains 16 species of pine. This collection is displayed on a gentle slope among previously existing plantings of Cotinus, ornamental Prunus, and several large cedars, enhanced with a background of oak woods and mature white pine. The Watnong Collection is directly south along Conifer Road, adjacent to, but still separate from, the Gotelli Collection.

Since the death of Don and Hazel Smith, the Watnong Nursery has been converted into a public garden through the dedication of their friends. Because of the Smiths' generousity, many of the plants they discovered had been given away. Efforts continue to locate plant material from the Watnong introductions to reassemble a comprehensive collection in the garden.

right and below: This pond was mainly built to provide drainage for the Gotelli Collection, which was planted on the side of a hill, and needed a catch basin. It is located near the northeast corner of the Collection, close to Conifer Road.

In addition to providing drainage, it also provides beauty and interest. By planting *Taxoidium distichum* 'Pendens' beside the pond, this interesting tree had the moisture it needed to develop its characteristic 'knees' – adding further to the 'interesting' part.

right: July 1973 – *below:* January 1994

above: The Gotelli Collection viewed from the air - July 1973.   photo courtesy of the USNA

I've provided a key to a few I could identify – The blue foliage of the *Picea pungens* culti-vars are the easiest to identify, and the huge *Cedrus atlantica* stands out in the crowd, so it was easy. It's a bit of a game, but you might enjoy referring to the current photos, so I've provided the page numbers after the cultivar names.

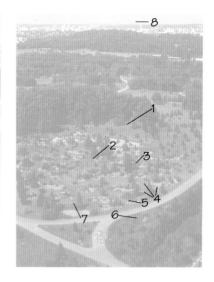

1 *Cedrus atlantica* 'Glauca' pgs 3-1,4,6&7
2 *Picea pungens* 'Hoopsii' pgs 2-13, 5-32
3 *Picea pungens* 'Pendula' pg 5-31
4 *Metasequoia glyptostroboides*
   'National' pgs1-6, 2-14
5 Bed 41 - pg 1-6
6 *Picea pungens* cv. pg 1-7
7 *Taxodium distichum* pgs 4-13, 5-46
8 Washington Monument

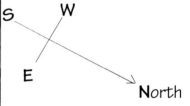

The Gotelli Conifer Collection

Donated in 1962 by William T. Gotelli, it is considered one of the most out-standing collections of its kind in the world. About 1500 specimens repre-senting 30 genera of dwarf and slow-growing conifers are planted on five acres at the northeast corner of the Arboretum.

The Watnong Collection of Pines

This Collection was presented to the Arboretum in 1979 by Donald and Ha-zel Smith, owners of the Watnong Nursery in Morris Plains, New Jersey. It is located on about an acre of high ground adjacent to the Gotelli Collec-tion, in the Northeast corner of the Arboretum, and includes 60 cultivars of 16 species of pine.

Private Donations Make a Difference

Many of the outstanding features at the Arboretum are the direct result of private benefactors, like Mr. Gotelli and the Smiths, and some are the result of a group doing fund-raising. Although foundations were not established for the continuing maintenance of either the Gotelli or the Watnong Collections, you can make a contribution to either or both Collections. Contact the Friends of the National Arboretum (see page 4-8).

Answers To   4
A Few Questions…

You don't see many books with answers to questions that haven't been asked –– This book is an exception. This chapter is a compilation of information that answered many of my questions, and maybe it will answer a few questions for you. Depending on how serious you are (or become) about gardening with dwarf and unusual conifers, the information presented here will seem more or less relevant. So, take a quick look-thru (so you'll know what's here), then, skip past the parts that don't interest you – yet.

Have you been wondering why some of the botanical names in this book ended with 'cv.'? Or it seemed like the cultivar name was missing after a species name? Or had slashes following the species name, i.e. '/sel./', '/'Zebrina' Mutant/', '/varient/'? And I won't tell you how long before I learned what 'cv. indet' stood for. These are some of the questions I had to ask, so I'm passing along the answers:

The 'cv.' following the species name indicates a cultivar does not have a botanical name assigned to it. The plant may be too similar to a named cultivar to warrant its own listing, it may be a new introduction under study, or maybe it has never been identified. It is an institutional designation used at the Arboretum for their plant records, and it has the same meaning in this book.

Species names are italicized and stand alone. When a species specimen (true species, not a cultivar) is listed along with the names of cultivars in the keys to the drawings, it might <u>look</u> like something is missing. It is the proper way to indicate a species according to botanical nomenclature (explained further on pages 4-4 through 4-7).

A name listed between slashes indicates there is some confusion regarding the proper name for the cultivar. Again, this is an institutional designation used at the Arboretum for their plant records. And 'cv. indet' stands for 'cultivar undetermined' – more current material receives the designation 'selection of'. This information is particularly relevant when you're at the Arboretum, inspecting the labels on a specimen, trying to determine its name!

Conifer Sizes

Conifer – Why so Technical?

The basic botanical distinction is between **broadleaf** and **conifer** when describing the two general categories of trees or shrubs. 'Conifer' is from a Latin word meaning "cone-bearing". With a few exceptions such as junipers and yews which have berry-like fruit, the production of cones is a common characteristic. The leaves are usually needle-shaped, awl-shaped, or scale-shaped; the exception being the broad, fan-shaped leaf of the ginkgo, a distant relative of the conifer family.

The common reference to conifers as 'evergreens', although usually understood in the same way many slang meanings are usually understood, can be misleading in a situation where specifics are necessary — particularly when you have an exact cultivar in mind. 'Evergreen' encompasses hollies, rhododendrons, azaleas, magnolias, boxwoods, viburnums, pyracanthas, cotoneasters, mountain laurels, heaths & heathers, mahonias, euonymus – to name a few that come to mind in my own yard – and all are broadleaf.

There are also deciduous (i.e., lose their leaves every year) conifers. Bald-cypress, dawn redwood, ginkgo and larch are all known for their unusual and often brilliant fall coloring before they drop their leaves — These are also 'evergreens' that, to many people, look like they die each winter! Although many people are referring to Christmas-type trees when they describe a tree as 'evergreen', when you want to purchase a specific plant, accurate communication is important.

When space is limited, plant size becomes an important issue. Appropriate size depends on the landscape situation, with sizes varying from minute mounds of elegant foliage to massive forest giants. In an effort to standardize size definitions, The American Conifer Society has adopted, as a relative guide, four size categories.

A particular cultivar's growth rate and ultimate size can vary, with many factors such as culture and climate influencing its growth. For instance, between the Pacific Northwest's ideal growing conditions, and the Northeast's severe weather extremes, a wide range of growth rates can be expected. So, as a general rule, the more ideal the growing conditions are, expect growth rates closer to the higher figures in each category. With more severe growing conditions, expect growth rates more towards the lower end figures.

Definitions – Relative Growth Rate/Size Guide*

Miniature Category is less than 3 inches growth per year.

Expected size at 10 - 15 years would be 2 - 3 feet.

Dwarf Category is 3 - 6 inches growth per year.

Expected size at 10 - 15 years would be 3 - 6 feet.

Intermediate Category is 6 - 12 inches growth per year.

Expected size at 10 - 15 years would be 6 - 15 feet.

Large Category is over 12 inches growth per year.

Expected size at 10 - 15 years would be over 15 feet.

*Resouce: The American Conifer Society web site:
http://www.pacificrim.net/~bydesign/acs.html

Conifer Forms

Form describes the general outline of the plant (see Definitions chart below). It is a major influencing factor in the choice of dwarf and unusual conifer cultivars. The wide range of form variations contributes to the popular appeal. That is to say, the quest seems to start innocently enough:

You decide upon a **globose** cultivar to enhance your mixed perennial border. Not much later, you get to thinking your **globose** cultivar might be set off nicely by a totally **prostrate** cultivar… Which in turn can lead to the 'need' for a **narrow upright** cultivar to lend a bit more perspective, and further help accentuate your **globose** cultivar's symmetrical form… Then, a bit later, it becomes obvious you 'need' to introduce something a bit less formal, maybe an **irregular** cultivar to balance things… and maybe a **broad upright** to lend weight. Soon you decide the overall appearance would be enhanced by the repetition of similar forms. Maybe a few more **globose** forms, along with two more **narrow uprights** – telling yourself that a group of three is more pleasing to the eye – justifying that your single **narrow upright** doesn't quite convey the feeling you are after, that it needs company…

Can you tell how this innocent hobby takes seed in people, and grows and grows, until it becomes a consuming passion? When you realize you have the 'symptoms', and are in need of therapy, join the ACS; you'll find yourself in good company. These folks understand!

Definitions – Conifer Forms (Outlines)*

Globose – Rounded.

Pendulous – Upright or mounding with varying degrees of weeping branches.

Narrow Upright – Much taller than broad; includes fastigiate, columnar, narrowly pyramidal, or narrowly conical.

Broad Upright – Includes all other upright plants that do not fit into one of the above categories.

Prostrate – Ground-hugging, carpeting plants, lacking a central leader. The best have no tendency to grow upward, can include slightly mounding.

Spreading – Wider than tall, often includes mounding.

Irregular – Erratic growth pattern.

Culturally Altered – Pruned or trained into formal or imaginative shapes. Includes high grafts and standards.

Conifer Form Examples**
(Page numbers listed in parentheses)

Globose –
Picea pungens 'Compacta' (2-1, 2-5), *Pinus sylvestris 'Riverside Gem'* (2-14,15), *Thujopsis dolabrata 'Nana'* (4-12, 5-48)

Pendulous –
Cedrus atlantica 'Glauca Pendula' (5-1,2,3,5,6,7), *Cedrus deodara 'Devinely Blue'* (2-8, 5-8), *Picea pungens 'Glauca Pendula'* (2-8, 5-31)

Narrow Upright –
Juniperus scopulorum 'Gray Gleam' (1-11), *Picea omorika 'Pendula'* (2-8, 2-15, 5-30), *Pinus sylvestris 'Spaan's Slow Column'* (2-8)

Broad Upright –
Cedrus atlantica 'Glauca' (3-1,6,7), *Chamaecyparis pisifera 'Squarrosa Intermedia'* (2-8, 3-9,10,11), *Pinus flexilis 'Vanderwolf's Pyramid'* (2-14), *Tsuga canadensis 'Brandley'* (2-8, 5-49)

Prostrate –
Juniperus conferta 'Blue Lagoon' (1-9, 5-21), *Juniperus procumbens 'Nana'* (1-11, 2-11, 1-16, 3-9, 5-23), *Picea pungens 'Glauca Prostrata'* (5-32)

Spreading –
Juniperus x media 'Plumosa Aurea' (2-5, 5-22,23), *Pinus resinosa Don Smith'* (1-15, 5-38), *Thuja occidentalis 'Hetz Midget'* (2-2, 5-47), *Thuja occidentalis 'Rheingold'* (5-47)

Irregular –
Cedrus libani 'Aurea Prostrata' (5-9), *Cedrus libania 'Green Prince'* (5-10), *Pinus parviflora 'Ei-Ko-nishiki'* (5-38)

**Only a sampling of examples – provided as a quick reference tool.

*Resouce:
The American Conifer Society web site: http://www.pacificrim.net/~bydesign/acs.html

What's in a Name — Some Conifer Definitions

A conifer is a woody plant that reproduces by fertile seeds formed within a cone. In evolution, the conifers came after the tree ferns and the cycads, plants with a two-stage reproduction cycle. Conifers preceded the broad-leafed flowering plants; the needle is to the conifer as the leaf is to the flowering plant. In theory, the needle is an adaptation to protect plants from drought and cold. In hot weather, plants transpire water through their leaves, and during periods of cold, dehydration occurs above ground due to the frozen earth and a plant's inability to take up water.

There are exceptions to needles, like the ginkgo tree (*Ginkgo biloba*) which dates back 180 million years and is closely related to conifers. This tree was widely distributed in prehistoric times with many species in the fossil record. Now only a single species survives. There are also deciduous conifers including, *Larix* or larch, *Metesequoia glyptostroboides* or dawn redwood, and *Taxodium distichum*, the bald cypress. Although most conifers have needles, it is the cone that is used for positive identification of a genus.

What's in a Name?

Common names may change from region to region while scientific or Latin names are consistent. The first word is always the genus; the second word is the specific epithet; together the genus and the specific epithet make the species name. If present, the third name is the variety, or, if in single quotes, the cultivar. The various names often refer to the discoverer, growth habit, place of origin, color, and other characteristics.

What's in a Name?

Common names may change from region to region while scientific or Latin names are consistent. The first word is always the genus; the second word is the specific epithet; together the genus and the specific epithet make the species name. If present, the third name is the variety, or, if in single quotes, the cultivar. The various names often refer to the discoverer, growth habit, place of origin, color, and other characteristics.

For example, *Juniperus procumbens* 'Nana' means a juniper with a trailing habit that is a dwarf; *Tsuga canadensis* 'Albospica' is a Canadian hemlock that bears a white tip; and *Tsuga canadensis* 'Cole's Prostrate' is a prostrate form discovered by Mr. Cole. Scientific names are always set in a type face that sets them apart from surrounding type styles. This usually means an italic type face.

Dwarfs vary in growing characteristics. Some take 20 to 30 years to reach a height of five feet. Others are slow at first but increase growth rate with age; others start fast and slow down later. Some offer unlimited use in today's landscapes, some are for collectors, and others are especially useful in small scree or rock gardens and troughs.

Dwarf conifers offer several positive characteristics. First, as smaller plants they fit into today's restricted landscapes. Secondly, growers and landscapers are looking for different plants to diversify their products and designs. Third, the public is becoming more educated and wants unusual plant material. And finally, these plants require less maintenance, including both pruning and general care. Humphry Welsh — considered by many conifer buffs to be the grandfather of dwarf conifers — once said that a dwarf was a plant he could see over in 20 years.

Written by Charlene Harris — Reprinted with permission.
Published Winter 1992 in *The American Conifer Society Bulletin*, Volume 9 No. 1.

Charlene Harris is the Editor and Managing Director for the *American Conifer Society Bulletin*. She is a horticultural instructor, lecturer and garden designer. Charlene has two gardens in Michigan; Brookstreet Gardens, a collector's nursery and home of 20 years in Ann Arbor, and a country lakeside home being developed as a natural wetland setting with a wildlife habitat garden near Chelsea. The two gardens include several hundred conifers collected over the past 20 years.

Examples of Genus Names

Abies = fir
Juniperus = juniper
Picea = spruce
Pinus = pine
Taxus = yew
Thuja = arborvitae
Tsuga = hemlock

Examples of Botanical Latin:

alba = white
chinensis = originated in China
cristata = crested
densis = thick
elegans = very pretty
erectus = upright
fastigatus = columnar
glauca = bluish gray
gracilis = graceful
humilis = low-growing
japonica = originated in Japan
lutea = pale yellow
macrophylla = large leaves/needles
microphylla = small leaves/needles
nana = dwarf
niger/nigra = black
pendula/pendulus = drooping
pyramidal = shaped like a pyramid
rotundifoilia = rounded leaves/needles
sempervirens = evergreen
spicata = flowers on a spike
variegata = variegated foliage
zebrinus = striped

Nomenclatural Basics

A classification system has been devised which divides the plant kingdom into progressively smaller groups or categories. The names for these groups are governed by an internationally accepted Code of Botanical Nomenclature and are as follows: division, class, order, family, genus, species, subspecies, variety, form. Intermediate categories may be formed by adding the prefix **sub-** to the preceding terms, for example: subfamily, subgenus, subspecies. Since living organisms do not always fit into rigidly defined categories, there is frequent disagreement among botanists as to what constitutes these categories. For example, a particular group of plants that appears to constitute a species to one botanist might be judged a variety by another. Horticulturists are often concerned with differences between plants that are not adequately distinguished by the preceding botanical categories. The term cultivar (cultivated variety) was coined to serve this purpose. The naming of cultivars is governed by a supplementary Code of Nomenclature for Cultivated Plants.

A **family** is a group of genera whose members resemble one another in several respects. Some families are large and some very small. The grass family (*Poaceae*) contains about 9,000 species in 650 genera. The ginkgo family (*Ginkgoaceae*) contains one genus and one species, *Ginkgo biloba*.

A **genus** (plural: genera) is made up of closely related and similar plant species. The rules of nomenclature state that all plants must have a binomial (two-parted) name consisting of the genus followed by the specific epithet (see below). The generic name is always capitalized.

The **specific epithet** follows the generic name, and together these two parts make up the species name of a plant. In the case of *Molinia caerulea*, *Molinia* is the genus, *caerulea* is the specific epithet, and *Molinia caerulea* is the name of the species. The specific epithet is normally not capitalized. A **species** (plural: species) is an assemblage of plants that are similar in a number of characteristics. Species are normally interfertile and breed true. A sugar maple seed grows into a sugar maple and a red maple seed grows into a red maple. Hybrids do occur in nature

Longwood Gardens

I talked to Bill Thomas, Education Division Manager at Longwood Gardens, when I was seeking permission to reprint this 'Nomenclatural Basics' article. I have visited Longwood: It is an amazing place, and I highly recommend you visit! I told Bill I would like to include a descriptive paragraph about Longwood, but how could Longwood possibly be described in one paragraph? He provided the following:

Longwood Gardens is one of the world's premier horticultural displays. Recalling the great pleasure gardens of Europe, Longwood combines horticulture, architecture, theatre, and music into a unique garden experience. Eleven thousand different types of plants flourish throughout 1,050 acres of formal gardens, fountains, idea gardens, meadows, and woodlands, with nearly four acres inside the Conservatory. There is something happening every day at Longwood; the Schedule of Events is filled with 700 performing arts and education programs.

but are uncommon. The word species may be abbreviated **sp.** (singular) or **spp.** (plural).

A **subspecies** differs from others of the same species in one or more characteristics and is often considered to have a recognizable geographic distribution within the range of the species. It may be abbreviated **subsp.** Subspecific epithets are normally not capitalized.

A botanical **variety** differs from others of the same species in one or a very few characteristics. For example, the flowers may be different in color or the leaves different in shape. A botanical variety may or may not have a clear geographical distribution. Varietal epithets are normally not capitalized. Botanical variety may be abbreviated **var.**

A **form** denotes minor genetic variants that sporadically occur in populations, such as the occasional pink-flowered dogwood that may be found in a normally white-flowered population. Formal epithets are normally not capitalized. Form may be abbreviated **f.**

A **cultivar**, or cultivated variety, is a group of plants under cultivation whose members differ from other members of the same species in one or more characteristics. A cultivar may derive from an abnormal individual in the wild, be developed by hybridization, or be selected under cultivation. It is maintained in cultivation by vegetative propagation or by selection because of its unique characteristics. Cultivar names should always be capitalized.

When inserted in text, generic, specific, subspecific, varietal and formal names should be set off by a typographic device such as italic or bold print or underlining. Cultivar names are not set off in such a way; however, they must be enclosed in single quotation marks or preceded by the abbreviation **cv.** For example, when inserted in text, the tall upright cultivar of purple moor grass may be written:

Molinia caerulea subsp. *arundinacea* 'Skyracer'
OR
Molinia caerulea subsp. arundinacea cv. Skyracer

Prepared by R. Darke, R. Herald and D. Huttleston, partly revised 9/94
Reprinted with permission of Longwood Gardens, Kennett Square, PA

The U.S. National Arboretum

The U.S. National Arboretum is a U.S. Department of Agriculture research facility and living museum dedicated to serving the public and improving our environment by developing and promoting improved landscape plants and new technologies through scientific research, educational programs, display gardens, and germplasm conservation. The Arboretum is a unique federal institution linked by partnerships to other governmental agencies, the scientific community, other arboreta and botanical gardens, and various private sector groups. It is a national center for public education that welcomes visitors in a stimulating and aesthetically pleasing environment.

The mission of the National Arboretum is to conduct research, provide education, conserve and display trees, shrubs, floral, and other plants to enhance the environment.

The Arboretum was established by an Act of Congress on March 4, 1927. It occupies 444 acres in the northeast section of the District of Columbia, with nine miles of paved roads providing access to the principal plant groups. The intermediate climatic zone makes it possible to grow trees and shrubs from a relatively wide range of growing conditions. Since 1927, the Arboretum has introduced over six hundred cultivars to the nursery trade.

Volunteers play an integral role in the Arboretum, where they participate and assist in almost every area and endeavor. Volunteers participate in a thorough training program, resulting in their efforts becoming an extension of the permanent staff. For instance, the 1996 season had more than 200 volunteers contributing thousands of hours to assist in preserving our National treasure!

FONA

Friends of the National Arboretum (FONA) is an independent, non-profit organization, established to enhance, through public and private sector resources, support for the U.S. National Arboretum. Many aspects of the continued success of the Arboretum are attributable to the public support given through FONA. FONA funds several much-needed full and part-time internships. They also produce a quarterly newsletter, *Arbor Friends*.

If you would like to make a gift or contribution to the Arboretum (you can specify particular gardens or collections), or want to know about membership, contact FONA, 3501 New York Avenue, NE, Washington, D.C. 20002-1958, (202) 544-8733.

Susan F. Martin, Horticulturist
Curator, Conifer, Dogwood & Maple Collections

Susan, accompanied by her dog, Kizzy, preparing plant material for one of the many requests she receives. Coming in on the weekend to make sure the order goes out, she says, "I'm not even supposed to be here – this is my day off – but sometimes the only way to make sure this gets done is to do it when it's quiet."

Who is Susan F. Martin?

Horticulturist — Curator of Conifer, Dogwood & Maple Collections

I thought you might like to know a bit more about Susan F. Martin, since I mention her so often throughout this book.

In 1979, Susan started her job as curator for the Gotelli Dwarf & Slow-Growing Conifer Collection. That first year she took part in the installation of the Watnong Pinetum Collection. She summarizes her job at the U.S. National Arboretum in the American Conifer Society Bulletin, Summer 1989, Vol.6, No.4; "Other than caring for 15 acres of conifers and maples, I promote the use of these plants through public lectures, tours and through various publications."

She is a strong supporter of the American Conifer Society, and has given freely of her time and energy. One of the original founding members of the ACS, she conducted its first annual meeting at the Arboretum, served 10 years on the ACS Board of Directors, and was co-editor for the American Conifer Society Bulletin for 2 years.

Among her many 'titles', she is the U.S. representative for the International Registration Authority for conifer cultivars. I took full advantage of this, making every effort possible to be 'nomenclaturally correct' in this book. She is incredibly patient!

Susan is an unassuming person, avoiding the limelight (which includes not liking her picture taken), yet she is not timid. She's quite willing to speak up, pitch in or even take over when the occasion calls for it. Her supervisor, Elizabeth Ley, said, "The reason Susan is so effective and dependable is that her ego doesn't get in the way -- whatever she is suggesting or doing is going to be in the best interest of the organization or situation because she is not seeking personal recognition. Her perception is much more insightful and reliable than the many folks who measure their actions by 'What's in it for me?'"

So if you haven't gathered this by now, I am extremely grateful to Susan Martin. She is always there for you, willing to do anything she can to help — and do it as soon as possible — as long as you're not trying to give her thanks, appreciation, compliments, medals, awards or make her the center of attention.

Susan F. Martin

Although her official title doesn't include teacher, Susan gives tours, patiently answers phone calls & letters, and gives slide presentations to various groups — generally available to teach whenever a person wants to learn! Her 'feel-good-feeling' is when she knows she's contributed to a person's education. In my case, she ought to feel really good, considering how much she's added to my education!

above: Conifer Road at the east end of the Gotelli Collection, looking north. The lush spray of spring foliage to the left is a branch of *Cedrus deodara* 'Aurea', appearing to hang over the entrance path to the Collection, and the 'Best of Beds' are on the right.

Visiting the ACS World Wide Web site:

I encourage you to visit the ACS web site. It's an extensive site, and new information continues to be added – plus they list quite a few links to other conifer-related sites.

below: Hazel Smith, January 20, 1983, attending the official organizational meeting of the American Conifer Society held at Joel Spingarn's home in Long Island, New York.

Photo courtesy of the USNA

The American Conifer Society
Founded in 1983

Goals:
- To encourage the development, conservation, and propagation of conifers, with emphasis on those that are dwarf or unusual.
- To aid in the standardization of conifer nomenclature.
- To educate the public.

Benefits:
Members receive four issues of the *ACS Bulletin*, an excellent publication that includes information on growing, finding, and caring for conifers. Also included are announcements of meetings and workshops, collector profiles, outstanding photographs, and advertisements.

One National Meeting per year is rotated through the regions. Locations are selected to provide access to interesting gardens and arboreta. Garden tours are an integral part of these meetings.

There are three Regions -- East, Central, and West -- each of which holds periodic meetings and offers workshops and garden tours. Often there are plant sales or auctions for members at these meetings.

The ACS is a friendly group of people. The majority are gardeners and plant lovers looking for special year-round interest and color in their gardens. In addition to hobby gardeners, there are members who are nationally and internationally prominent horticulturists, botanists and plant hunters. New members, guests and novices are always welcome. This is a knowledgable group of friendly folks, very willing to share. My experience has been that you don't realize a person is a 'prominent' member of the horticultural world until you hear them speak as part of the program... These folks are not there to toot their own horn, but to share in this special pool of knowledge and experience – and to have a lot of fun. And these 'down-to-earth' folks do know how to have fun!

Membership Contact:

The American Conifer Society
P.O. Box 360
Keswick, VA 22947-0360
(804) 984-3660 (Voice & FAX)

Visit the ACS World Wide Web site:

http://www.pacificrim.net/~bydesign/acs.html

above: To achieve contrasts like the photo above, it is important to consider the color of the fall foliage when choosing deciduous companion plants.

Companion Plants

Companion plants for dwarf and unusual conifers are desirable because they can enhance, compliment, balance, and/or highlight the many colors, forms and textures of conifers. Japanese maples, heaths, heathers, miniature roses, small shrub roses, azaleas and miniature rhododendrons are all good companion plants. Also perennials such as herbs, dianthus, ajuga, ferns, grasses, lilies, hostas, sedums, and many others make excellent companion plants.

Because of the relative ease of transplanting, perennials are particularly versatile as fill-in companion plants while dwarf conifers mature. Artemisia, dianthus and herbs are three groups of perennials that I use extensively. What I like about them is that they compliment without taking over – and if they do become too intrusive or overwhelming, they are easy to yank out (that part is important).

Dwarf varieties are available for many shrubs such as barberry, boxwood, holly, lilac, mountain laurel, and spirea. Reviewing the many companion plants in my own yard, and thinking in terms of shrubs that stay within bounds, I realized that many are of Japanese origin. The Japanese have been breeding plants for diminutive size for hundreds of years, and many are readily available throughout the U.S.

I singled out several of the U.S. National Arboretum's Elite Plant Introductions from Japan as examples of companion plants. When I learned about these particular plants, I already had several in my own garden, and found it interesting to realize I was an active participant in this successful program. All these plants are readily available, easily managed, and a desired size can be easily maintained. Look for these same characteristics when choosing other companion plants for dwarf and unusual conifers.

A Few USNA Elite Plant Introductions

The following list of USNA Introductions is a sampling of good companion plants for dwarf and unusual conifers.

Hydrangea macrophylla 'Nigra'– Pink or blue flowers, depending on soil pH, bloom June & July; stem color is nearly black; partial shade; 3-5'; z6-9

Ajania pacifica–Button-like clusters of golden yellow flowers in late October; grayish green leaves with silver edge and back; full sun;low growing perennial; z4-8

Ilex crenata 'Sky Pencil'–Narrow growing evergreen shrub; full sun to partial shade; 7 to 10 feet; z6b

Deutzia gracilis 'Nikko'–White flowers cover it in May; full sun or partial shade; low growing deciduous shrub, 12-18" high, spreading with age; z5-8

Euonymus japonica 'Green Spire'– lossy dark green evergreen leaves; narrow columnar form; full sun or partial shade; to 10' or more; z7-9

Miscanthus sinensis 'Morning Light'– Gently arching narrow leaf blades with white edge and silver midrib; attractive fall seed heads; full sun; to 5'; z5

The beautiful large specimen behind the bench is *Pinus nigra* 'Globosa' – Note its rounded crown, dense clusters of foliage, and the striking color and interesting outline of its multi-trunks. In front and immediately below *P.n.* 'Globosa' is *Thujopsis dolabrata* 'Nana'; the full pyramidal form to the right of *P.n.* 'Globosa' is *Pinus heldreichii* var. *leucodermis*; and the small, bright flash of gold in the background, directly above the middle of the bench, is *Chamaecyparis obtusa* 'Elmwood Gold'.

Other Gardens to Visit

I recommend your first visit be The American Conifer Society's web page (see page 4-10) for a listing of display gardens and arboretums with conifer collections. It is sorted by regions – eastern, central, western – which I found helpful.

Sources -

Sources - Note
There is another option if you want a listing of sources for dwarf and unusual conifers: You can send a stamped, self-addressed envelope along with two dollars for handling ($2.00) to the author, c/o the publisher, P.O. Box 802, North Olmsted, OH 44070-0802. Although I make every effort to keep the listing up-to-date, I cannot guarantee the list is all-inclusive. Please note whether you are interested in the mail order, retail or wholesale listing.

Your local garden center can be a source of dwarf and unusual conifers. In the four years it's taken to put this book together, I have noticed quite an increase in the selections available at local garden centers. Within an hour's drive of my home there are several specialty nurseries with dwarf and unusual conifers, which would be true of many large metropolitan areas. As popular demand increases, more choices will become available.

Contact the American Conifer Society (see page 4-10). The advertising in the ACS Bulletin provides sources for retail, mail-order, and wholesale. You might want to have your garden center order a particular cultivar from one of the advertised wholesale nurseries.

Visit the ACS's web site for up-to-date sources (see page 4-10).

Do you have A.C.S.?
(Addicted Conifer Syndrome)
by Susan Eyre

Rich and I recently attended the Fifth Annual ACS Central Region gathering for those with A.C.S. - Addicted Conifer Syndrome. The Central Region is well known for the Support Group offered to those phytoholics with a unique weakness for the search and research of mutuant conifers. At the 1995 ACS National Meeting in North Carolina, there were even meetings for the families of those who are addicted (mainly at shopping malls). Many people ask "Can you get hooked the first time?" Absolutely! When analyzed, there are several levels of addiction to those who are powerless about these plants.

Level 1: Awareness
This is the initial phase where in some way, garden conifers are brought to your attention. It could be a magazine article on Ed Rezek or maybe a television program on the Victory Garden about Ed Rezek. Perhaps you were visiting a place that featured interesting conifers. Rich and I literally stumbled into the Hidden Lake Gardens and found 'The Harper Collection* of Rare and Dwarf Conifers' by accident. Needless to say, it changed our lives.

Level 2: Research
After the initial awareness, you start researching conifers. This is not an easy task for there is no one book or place to obtain all the information. It may start out innocently, reading about the Redwoods, Giant Sequoias, Bristlecones or Ginkgos. You join the American Conifer Society (ACS) for information and eventually the ACS Bulletin becomes the most exciting magazine you get! Krüssmann, van Hoey Smith, Swartley, and Welch appear on your Christmas list.

Level 3: Acquisition
Reading about these conifers is simply not enough. You must have them! You try your local garden centers and perhaps you find a dwarf Alberta spruce at K-Mart®. Tree dreams are common at this level. You find yourself driving longer distances to get to nurseries to purchase unusual plants. Many people are extremely willing to drive a whole day to buy one tree! Family vacations are arranged around these places and addiction is evident by the vacation photos where there are more plants than people in the pictures. The ultimate rationalization occurs before the ACS Auction. On your way to the auction you say "I'm not going to spend much at the auction this year." On the way home you mention "The money went for a good cause."

Level 4: Networking
Now you have a small collection started but you are still not satisfied. The ACS leads you to other people who have the same affliction. Beware of those who have lifetime memberships. There are two type of family members of those with A.C.S. The 'enablers' take care of business or family matters at home so

Do you have A.C.S.? (Continued)

the addicted can network alone at the meetings. The 'co-dependents' come to the meetings with the addicted and they blend in with the coniferites. Problems begin to occur when you attend a family wedding in Washington D.C. but you arrive to the reception late because you had to go see the Gotelli Collection one more time!

Level 5: Reading the Landscape

Now that you are integrated into the conifer network, you start reading the landscape and looking for witches brooms in nature. Driving becomes more dangerous for 'Baby Broomers' as you are looking for brooms instead of watching traffic. Add plenty of extra travel time on trips so you can stop at every cemetery between here and there. It is devastating when another coniferite comes into your territory and instantly finds a broom you missed in your own neighborhood. Observation skills are developed.

Level 6: Propagation

Perhaps the ACS Seed Exchange excites you and you write for seeds. Or you find a great broom. You can't continue to just admire it...you want to know "Could this be a new cultivar of the future?" This is where graft and corruption set in. At this level, there is 'mail-bonding'. There are packages coming and going in the mail at all levels of urgency: UPS, FedEx, Overnight, Priority Mail. You start grafting or rooting conifers.

Level 7: Going into Business

You have now reached the pinnacle of the addiction. You have made your hobby your livelihood. Now any tree purchase can be justified! It's a stock plant! Now there is satisfaction in helping distribute these beauties to the addicted.

Level 8: Benefactor

At this level you have spent a big part of your wallet collecting conifers. Now you start relocating your collection and you buy conifers to give away. This is the 'Harper Predilection' and difficult to explain to your wife.

Whatever level you are, join in on the fun and <u>JUST SAY YES</u>!

Do you have A.C.S.?
(Addicted Conifer Syndrome)
Reprinted with permission
from the author and the publisher.

Descriptions
Cultivars – Species

5

Descriptions in this chapter are estimates based on growing conditions at the U.S. National Arboretum, Washington, D.C. (USNA and/or the Arboretum). The soil is 'Christiana Sunnyside' – deep soils with unstable clayey sediment. Rainfall varies year to year, averaging 47 inches per year, but with some summers including months of drought conditions. The summers are hot and humid, often remaining hot at night. The winters rarely have snow cover for even a few days, and usually receive cold, desiccating winds. It takes a pretty hardy specimen to thrive given these conditions.

The Gotelli Collection was donated in 1962, and there are well over **three hundred** of the original Gotelli Collection plants still growing at the Arboretum. William Gotelli had been collecting for fifteen years prior to donating his collection to the USNA. These 'survivors' are 35 years old as of 1997 – plus however many years old they were when they were donated – this definitely speaks for their hardiness!

Hardiness at USNA

'Hardiness' at the Arboretum often means whether that cultivar can tolerate the hot, humid summers, although cold hardiness is a factor with some genera. Colder mountainous regions are the native habitat for the majority of conifers. Most conifer species from the warmer temperate or sub-tropical zones cannot survive the cold winters of Washington, D.C., consequently only the more hardy of the warmer temperate

Cedrus atlantica 'Glauca Pendula'

This is not a dwarf — But it certainly is unusual! The form & shape it takes on depends on training. This unique feature at the SW end of the Gotelli Collection, overlooks most of the Collection. With a little imagination, the right light and angle, it can take on the appearance of a dragon. Ed Rezek, an avid conifer collector, has *C.a.* 'Glauca Pendula' draped all around his home, with the limbs hanging like silver icicles. An amazing planting at the Kubota Gardens in Seattle, Washington, is actually three separate trees appearing as one, taking up an enormous space, and forming a fairytale-like labyrinth of trails under its canopy of limbering branches. It is explored and enjoyed by many young visitors (of all ages) to the Gardens.

species are represented at the Arboretum. The zone ('z') listing given at the end of each description is an <u>estimate</u> of cold hardiness. Because there are so many variables involved in the question of hardiness, these listings must be considered <u>guidelines</u> only.

Species Descriptions Included

Brief descriptions of the species are included as an aid in understanding the general cultural requirements and hardiness of cultivars of that particular species. For more extensive information about the various species, be sure to refer to the 'Recommended Reading List.' Knowing if a species is native to a cold mountainous region, or a mild, semi-tropical region can be helpful in understanding the most beneficial growing conditions for the cultivars of that species.

For instance, a cultivar of a species native to a tropical environment would not be expected to perform well in areas with severe winters. By the same token, cultivars of species native to high mountainous areas with extremely cold winters seldom fare well in moderate climates. When considering a particular cultivar, be sure to get confirmation about its hardiness before purchasing.

Estimated Growth Rates

The height and width (−'H/−'W) given is the estimated average growth at ten years, unless otherwise noted. I've made an effort to include the estimated/approximate/average yearly growth rate (−'/yr). When using these figures as guidelines, realize there are many variables: Many conifers have rapid growth when they're young, then slow as they mature. Others take several years to get established, then you may see relatively rapid growth. Realize that a cultivar with a growth rate of 1-3"/yr, 25'/UH, can be enjoyed for a couple decades as a small shrub, because the ultimate height of 25' is going to be 'a long time a'comin'.

Also, many/most conifers tend to grow more vigorously in the Pacific Northwest than in Washington, D.C. More 'variables' that can influence growth rate are drainage, exposure, heat, cold, humidity, water, and soil condition — to name just a few. As a general rule, milder climates — like those in much of the Northwest — result in more rapid growth rates plus fuller foliage; while more severe climates — such as those in much of the Northeast — sparse growth and slower growth rates are more 'normal'.

Key to Descriptions

The descriptions are generally organized as follows:

Botanical name — common name (listed under each species); foliage color, shape and outstanding characteristics; overall form and growth characteristics; unusual or unique characteristics or requirements; sun/shade requirements; growth rates when available — average growth rate per year ('/yr'), expected height & width ('H/W') in ten years, ultimate height ('/UH'); minimum cold hardiness zone ('z'). Country of origin (species only).

The '*g' after the botanical name indicates it is shown in a group photo in an earlier chapter (see Index). Many of the 'NOTE' entries are contributions from Susan Martin, given as clarification or points of interest in answer to my questions.

Chosen Photos Are Just A Sampling

In order to have a **thorough** description of each cultivar, this chapter would need at least 3-5 photos of each species/cultivar, showing the form, branch habit, foliage closeup, cone closeups of both male & female cones in their various stages, candling and/or new foliage closeups, plus seasonal changes. My most difficult task in the compilation of this book was choosing what to leave out. I wanted to show it all!

The description photos that have been included show a sampling of the variations/similarities of cultivars within the given species, plus the differences/similarities between the different species. Hopefully, it will be an aid in your ability to make more 'educated' choices, plus give you a curiosity and desire to learn more about these fascinating plants.

Endless Variety - Constant Change

Each time I've visited the Arboretum, I've been overwhelmed with the changes and many stages of growth of the various conifers.

No matter what time of year I've visited, there is always a 'show' I hadn't seen before. The various species and cultivars put on 'shows' at different times — and just when I'm sure I've seen a speciman at its absolute most exquisite, I get to see it at a later/earlier season even more beautiful!

There is the 'candling', the cones in their many stages of growth (the male cones are often spectacular!), the flush of new growth, and the seasonal color changes. Quite amazing! (And I'm the one who dreaded adding 'evergreens' to our landscape because I thought of them as too common & boring! Plus, I dreaded having them overwhelm my landscape as they matured. . . Have I learned a thing or two!) No matter how many photos are shown & how thorough the descriptions, there is no way it could be enough: You will need to visit the Arboretum yourself . . . often.

Conifers Coming of Age
Abies

Abies pinsapo 'Glauca'
top: end of winter foliage – early March.
bottom: male pollen cones – early May.

Abies (genus) [A-beez] − Fir; genus contains about 50 species; its appearance is similar to and often confused with *Picea* (spruce); the foliage is usually soft to the touch (thinking of soft fur helped me remember the difference between *Abies* & *Picea* (prickly); the needles leave slight depressions in the stem when removed, leaving it smooth to the touch (unlike *Picea*'s stem, which is prickly); the cones are carried upright (the *Picea*'s cones hang downward); symmetrical conical form, lower branches falling away with maturity; tall tree, with some species reaching 300'+; prefers moist soils in areas of high rainfall; native from the Arctic Circle to the warm temperate regions of the Northern Hemisphere, but only found in the higher mountains toward their southern limits; about 2/3's of the species are native to Asia, most the others occur in North America.

Abies nephrolepis (species) [nef-ro-LEP-is] − Khinghan Fir, East Siberian Fir; thin, narrow, fresh yellow-green needles; small tree, 45-50' tall; susceptible to late frosts; z3 Manchuria (northeast China)

Abies pinsapo (species)[pin-SOP-o] − Spanish Fir, Hedgehog Fir; dark green, rigid-looking foliage; dense, broadly pyramidal form; to 65'; z7 southern Spain

Abies pinsapo 'Glauca' − rigid, thick, powder blue needles; broad, stately pyramidal tree; full sun; 6-12"/Y, 5-6'H/2-3'W, 60'/UH; z5 [male cones]

Cedrus (genus) [SED-rus] − Cedar; stiff, angular needles, 1"+ long, scattered on long shoots, clustered on the short spurs which project from branches; 3" long cones stand upright on branches; tall, irregularly branched; graceful in appearance; *atlantica, brevifolia, deodara* and *libani* are the 4 species in the genus *Cedrus*; native to Mediterranean region and Himalayas

Cedrus atlantica (species) − aka C.a. 'Glauca', (Blue) Atlas Cedar; powder blue needle-like leaves less than 1" long (needles shorter than C. deodara); sparse, ascending branches give conical form as young tree; as it matures, it becomes denser, lower branches becoming more horizontal, forming a broad pyramid; heat and drought tolerant; full sun; 12-24"/Y, 10-12'H/4-5'W, 120'/UH; z6 mountains of North Africa.

Cedrus atlantica 'Fastigiata' *g− blue-green needles, dense, upward reaching branches form narrow column; full sun; 12-24"/Y, 10-12'H/5'W; z6

Cedrus atlantica 'Glauca'
− mature cone
Photo courtesy USNA

Cedrus atlantica 'Glauca' − young cone

Cedrus atlantica 'Glauca Pendula' spring foliage shown at the center of the tree – the trunk on this specimen is massive!

Cedrus atlantica 'Glauca Pendula' – early spring as hints of new foliage appear on the deciduous trees in the background.   Photo by Susan Martin

Cedrus atlantica 'Glauca Pendula' spring foliage & draping habit
                Photo courtesy USNA

Cedrus atlantica 'Glauca Pendula' – early morning in late winter. Part of the original Collection, this amazing specimen measured 4' when it was placed in 1964. The tall, whispy outline in the center of the photo is *Pinus wallichiana* 'Zabrina'. She was a prominent feature in the Gotelli Collection for over 30 years.

Cedrus deodara 'Aurea' – newly emerging spring foliage

Cedrus atlantica **'Glauca Pendula'** — Weeping Blue Atlas Cedar; clusters of powdery steel-blue needles; extremely pendulous branches, cascading wherever trained — needs training or will grow prostrate on ground; slow-growing, but <u>not</u> a dwarf; full sun; 6-12"/Y, H/W depend on training; z6

Cedrus deodara (species) — Himalayan Cedar; silvery, bluish-green needle-like foliage to 2" long; wide spreading, arching branches; fast growing, becoming a large, pyramidal shaped tree; full sun; 10-16'H/7-10'W; Himalayas

Cedrus deodara **'Aurea'** *g— Golden Himalayan Cedar; long, soft golden foliage; cream-yellow new growth; graceful, drooping branches; soft pyramidal form; slow-growing but <u>not</u> a dwarf; full sun; 12-16"/Y, 6-7'H/2-3'W, 60'UH; z6

Cedrus deodara 'Aurea' – gracefully drooping branchs showing the fresh coloring of spring's new growth. This cultivar's coloring is most outstanding in spring with the new growth highlighting the branch tips of the entire tree. It is almost like a glowing beacon when observed from a distance.

Conifers Coming of Age
Cedrus deodara

Cedrus deodara 'Devinely Blue'

NOTE: *Cedrus deodara* 'Devinely Blue' – It really is spelled with 'e'; named by Don Howse of Porterhowse Farms, for Bill Devine, Maryland, who found this plant and gave it to the Arboretum. It's 'name' was *C.d.*/low spreading selection/ until Don had been propagating it for approx. 10 yrs., and felt it was such a special cultivar that it needed its own name.

The Northwest estimated growth rate is 3-6"/yr — the 2"/yr experienced at the Arboretum certainly illustrates the climatic differences!

Cedrus deodara **'Devinely Blue'** *g– blue-green to powder blue needles; drooping branch tips; wide-spreading, flat-topped shrub; full sun; grows as broad as tall, 2"/Y, 2'H/4'W; z6

Cedrus deodara **'Limelight'** *g– light green, drooping branches with lime/white new growth; pyramid form; full sun; 6-7'H/2-3'W; z6

Cedrus deodara **'Pendula'** *g– Weeping Himalayan Cedar; long, dark blue-green needles; requires staking when young; ideal specimen plant; full sun; not a dwarf - grows 12"/yr, H/W depend on staking; z6

Cedrus deodara **'Pygmy'** – bluish-green ½" needles; extremely slow-growing bun form; full sun; ½"/Y, 6-8"H/W; 18"H/24"W in 30 yrs; z5

Cedrus deodara **'Repandens'** – blue-green needles; very pendulous, branches procumbent; full sun; 12"/yr; z6

Cedrus libani (species) *g– Cedar of Lebanon; dark or bright green leaves to 1-1/4"long; broadly pyramidal to 120' with massive trunk; Asia Minor, Syria.

Cedrus libani **'Aurea Prostrata'** *g– bright gold color on bluish needles; grows upward at an angle, giving a windswept appearance; partial shade; 3-4'H/2'W; z5

Cedrus libani **'Green Prince'** *g– small, dark green needles grow in bunches, covering the branches — even the trunk; each branch grows in an irregular, artful and unique way, giving it the appearance of great age — has a natural Bonsai appearance; full sun; 1"/Y, 4'H/2'W; z6

Cedrus libani **'Nana'** *g– dense, light green foliage; upright globe form; full sun; 6-12"/Y, 2-3'H/24-30"W, 10'H/5'W in 35 yrs; z6

Cedrus libani subsp. *stenacoma* *g– short, dark gray-green needles; horizontal branches that start at the ground; an abundance of upright cones as the tree ages — the cones are striking, brilliant purple when they first appear, but quickly turn brown; pyramidal form; more cold hardy than the species; full sun; 20' in 30 yrs; z5

above: Cedrus deodara 'Limelight' (planted in the Watnong Collection in 1985) with three *Pinus pumila* selections

right: Cedrus deodara 'Pendula' – Spring foliage – early May

preceeding page –
Cedrus atlantica 'Glauca Pendula'
  left background– *Cedrus atlantica* 'Glauca'
  right foreground – *Pinus strobus* 'Elf'

Cedrus libani 'Aurea Prostrata'

– Two views of the same specimen. It takes on a different look, depending on which angle you see it. Though a newer addition to the Gotelli Collection, it's a mature specimen at 15+ years old. Each plant will be an original – no two of this cultivar will look alike – each becoming a unique art form.

Cephalotaxus harringtonia '**Korean Gold**' – 1-1/2" long flat gold needles in whorles; fastigiate form; full sun; 2-3"/Y; z7

Cephalotaxus harringtonia var. *drupacea* '**Duke Gardens**' *g– Japanese Plum Yew 'Duke Gardens'; deep green foliage throughout year; flattened leaves are two-ranked on the branches when planted in shade, as if waiting for any ray of sunshine they can get – in full sun it can afford the luxury of being whorled on the branches, so has a much fuller appearance; somewhat similar in appearance to English Yew with longer, more course, flat needles; horizontal branchlets, slightly ascending branches; slow-growing, dense, broad spreading habit without a central leader; shade; 6"/Y, 4'H/ 8'W in 20 yrs; z7

Cedrus libani 'Green Prince' – late winter foliage

*Cedrus deodara 'Pendula' –
above: male pollen cones – early May
left: Fall foliage – October*

Cedrus libani 'Green Prince', early March, with snow decorating its branches, showing off its artistic form.

NOTE: When I was first making plans for this book, I told Susan Martin I'd like to show several cultivars in different seasons, including a few shots with snow. — I live in northeast Ohio, which means I've got to plan my trips to Washington, D.C. — She answered, "You have a chance in a million of getting shots with snow. We hardly ever know ahead of time exactly when we'll get snow, and when/if we do, it usually only stays on the ground a few hours."

My favorite 'shot' of *Cedrus libani 'Green Prince'* — his background sparkling with prisms of light.

Mid-April, spring is just starting at the Arboretum – new growth is beginning to appear, highlighting the branch tips. Glimpsed from a distance, the whole plant sparkles.

This particular March, my stay was for a whole week, with the plan to have enough time to get the shots I still wanted – – I was hoping for snow. It started snowing the first day, shortly after I arrived at the Arboretum. I got some wonderful shots! From that time on, when I was making a trip to D.C., Susan would ask me what kind of weather I needed – – so she'd know what to expect…and would I please let her know if I was hoping for snow!

June at the Arboretum – late spring or early summer, depending on the year – Grasses are beginning to grow, and *C.l. 'Green Prince'* is merging with the landscape; not making a loud statement, but still very much an important part of the whole.

Beginning of May – new growth tufts of foliage fill in spaces along the mature branches and trunk. The new growth is soft & velvety to the touch, calling out, 'Reach out & touch me' – something we refrain from doing at the Arboretum, or the branches would be bare from petting. So you do like I did – Go back home and add one to your own garden.

I was especially fortunate to have the weather 'cooperating' as often as it did!

C.l. 'Green Prince' doesn't have the outstanding seasonal changes like some cultivars, but as you can see from these photos, a strong specimen plant can 'look' different with the seasonal changes of its surroundings.

Cedrus libani 'Green Prince' is beginning to take center stage again in fall (mid to late October most years) as the grasses take on their golden hue – – a perfect backdrop for *C.l. 'Green Prince'*.

Spring – early May. *front right center: Cephalotaxus harringtonia var. drupacea* 'Duke Gardens', *right: Picea glehnii, left: Picea orientalis* 'Gowdy', *front: Juniperus procumbens* 'Nana', *and center back: Stewarti pseudocamellia* — great companion plant! It blooms in June with 2-2½ white blossoms, has outstanding fall color, plus colorful exfoliating bark as it matures.

Fall colors

Photo by Susan Martin

Cephalotaxus harringtonia var. drupacea 'Duke Gardens'

Tolerates a wider range of soils than *Taxus* (heavier & wetter). USNA introduced — just starting to show up in trade (ask for it if you don't see it – it might be on its way or could be special ordered).

BONUS –
   deer don't seem to care for it!

Cephalotaxus harringtonia 'Korean Gold'

– Winter Protection –
Cephalotaxus harringtonia 'Korean Gold'
Fastigiate forms tend to split open with age (*C.h.* 'Korean Gold' is a fastigiate form) — binding in winter may help prevent this. Benefits from winter protection because it is susceptible to wind burn.

Chamaecyparis (genus), [kam-a-SIP-a-ris] — False Cypress; leaves are scale-like, in closely overlapping pairs on flaring sprays of branchlets ('adult'); leaves of some varieties are spine like, called 'juvenile', & sometimes confused with junipers; tall, conical form; seeds are prone to variation which provides an important source of unusual cultivars; two species native to western North America, one native to eastern United States, other species native to Japan and Taiwan.

Chamaecyparis lawsoniana (species) [law-sow-nee-A-nuh] — Lawson Cypress; green or glaucous scale-like leaves; branchlets flattened and frond-like in horizontal planes; columnar to pyramidal tree, 150-200'; native Oregon to northern California

NOTE: All Lawson Cypress benefit from mulching and prefer moist, well-drained soil, plus, they need protection from winter wind.

Conifers Coming of Age
Chamaecyparis lawsoniana

Chamaecyparis lawsoniana 'Pembury Blue'

Chamaecyparis nootkatensis 'Pendula'

Chamaecyparis obtusa 'Chilworth' – close to 3'H/2½'W in about 30 yrs

Chamaecyparis obtusa 'Crippsii'

Chamaecyparis lawsoniana 'Little Spire' — blue-grey foliage in tight sprays; narrow columnar form; full sun; 1-2"/Y; z5

Chamaecyparis lawsoniana 'Oregon Blue' — aqua blue foliage; tips of branches weeping; columnar form; fast growing; full sun; 12-24"/yr; z5

Chamaecyparis lawsoniana 'Pembury Blue' — striking bright silver-blue foliage held upright in loose vertical sprays; broad columnar growth habit; full sun; 6-12"/yr; 8-10'H/4'W; z5

Chamaecyparis nootkatensis (species) — Nootka Cypress, Alaska Cypress; dark green foliage forms overlapping sprays of branchlets that hang gracefully from swooping branches, when seen from a distance, give a fern-like appearance to the foliage; pyramidal tree to 120' or more; Alaska to Oregon.

Chamaecyparis nootkatensis 'Pendula' — Weeping Alaska Cypress; curtain of dark grey-green foliage on pendulous branchlets; upright tree with graceful, widely spaced, sweeping branches; considered one of the most elegant weeping specimen trees; it makes a striking specimen; full sun; 12-24"/yr, 6-7'H/3-4', 30'H/10-12'W in 35 yrs; z5

Chamaecyparis obtusa (species) — Hinoki Cypress; lustrous dark green scale-like foliage with rounded, slightly drooping tips on horizontal branchlets; broadly pyramidal tree; 75-120'/UH; z4 Japan

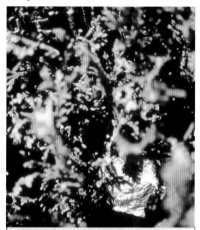

Hinoki Cypress or Juniper?

Chamaecyparis obtusa cultivar selections – The fan-shaped foliage above is more typical of Hinoki cypress, though there are quite a few cultivars such as the one on the right, with foliage similar to the junipers. You can tell the difference by touching them – junipers 'bite' – Hinoki cypress is pleasant to touch.

above: The praying mantis case is indicative of the success of the integrated pest management program at the Arboretum.

Chamaecyparis obtusa 'Chilworth' *g— small, fine textured, bright green foliage; very dwarf, bun shaped with a rounded top; full sun; ½"/yr; z5

Chamaecyparis obtusa 'Contorta' — highly convoluted, twisting dark green foliage; slow-growing, very dwarf, conical form; full sun; 18"H/3'W in 20 yrs; z4

Chamaecyparis obtusa 'Coralliformis' — twisted thread-like green foliage; unique texture; slow growing, dwarf bush form; full sun; to 8'H8W, 12'H/6'W in 35 yrs; z4-8

Chamaecyparis obtusa 'Crippsii' *g— sprays of feathery, golden-yellow foliage on frond-like, spreading branches; excellent winter color; pyramidal form; full sun/light shade; 6-12"/yr; 10'H/4'W; z4

Chamaecyparis obtusa 'Elf' — extremely small fine-textured foliage; forms a dwarf globe with little peaks on top; full sun; extremely slow growing, ½-1"/yr; 12"H&W; z5

Chamaecyparis obtusa 'Ericoides' — blue-green juvenile foliage; the new growth is glossy light green, turning plum-purple in winter, adding seasonal interest; dense, conical form; full sun; 1-1/2"/yr, 6'H/2'W; z5

Chamaecyparis obtusa 'Gracilis' — rich, dark green sculptured foliage; pyramidal form with slender, graceful pendulous branch tips; full sun; 6"/yr; 8'H/3'W; z5

Chamaecyparis obtusa 'Graciosa' — bright green, lacy, frond-like leaf sprays; upright globose form; partial shade; 3-6"/yr, 12'H/5'W; z4

Chamaecyparis obtusa 'Intermedia' *g— compact light green sprays of foliage; spreading globose, almost flat form; full sun; ½-3/4"/yr; z5

Chamaecyparis obtusa 'Kanaamihiba' — fka C.p. 'Squarrosa Kanaami-Hiba'; stout, threadlike golden foliage on thickened branches; tips appear contorted, usually with cockscomb-like clusters; irregular upright form; partial shade; 1-1½"/yr; z5

Chamaecyparis obtusa 'Kosteri' — cupped, scale-like, bright green foliage; slightly twisting sprays of foliage curl downward at the tips; ascending branches; upright compact form; partial shade; 1-3"/yr, 30-36"H/18-24"W; z4

Chamaecyparis obtusa 'Mariesii' — somewhat threadlike, scale-like variegated foliage, yellowish to white in sun, more creamy/yellow in shade; slow-growing globe form; full sun/partial shade; 1-3"/yr, 4'H/3'W in 15 yrs; z5

Chamaecyparis obtusa 'Nana' — dark green fine-textured foliage forms beautifully twisting fan-shaped branchlets growing in dense, tiered layers; very slow-growing, compact, flattened globe form; partial shade; 1"/yr, 10"H/10"W; z4

Chamaecyparis obtusa 'Nana Aurea' — bright yellow cupped sprays of foliage, bronze tone in winter; irregular pyramidal form; partial shade; 3'H/2'W; z5

Chamaecyparis obtusa 'Nana Gracilis' — glossy, dark green, compact cupped shaped foliage; upright form; irregular outline, becoming broadly conical with age — dwarf, but not a pygmy — grows rapidly when young, slows down with maturity; full sun/partial shade; 3'H/15"W; z4-8

Chamaecyparis obtusa 'Nana Lutea' — golden cup-shaped foliage, holds yellow & gold color all year in sun; gold-green color in shade; fan-shaped branch tips curving slightly downward; irregular-topped, broadly pyramidal mound; full sun for color; 3" per yr, 20"H/30"W; z5

Chamaecyparis obtusa 'Pygmaea' — sprays of flat, slightly fan-shaped foliage is glossy-green in summer, slightly bronze in winter; conspicuous orange-brown stems; dense, almost perfectly round globe form; full sun; 3'H&W; z5

Chamaecyparis obtusa 'Reis Dwarf' *g— irregular mounds of bright green very fine textured foliage; irregular, somewhat pyramidal form; light green branchlets twisting outward from the main body of the tree — these are not reversions; full sun; 1"/yr, varies from 18"H/30"W to 3-4'H/2-3'W in 10 yrs; z4

Chamaecyparis obtusa 'Ericoides' – (...and that lady bug is a good sign!)

Chamaecyparis obtusa 'Crippsii' – It does get BIG! It is slow-growing, but not dwarf. The specimen in the Gotelli Collection at 30+ years has two main trunks 20'H/12"W.

Chamaecyparis obtusa 'Gracilis' is a beautiful cultivar, and this particular plant is an especially handsome specimen, but this photo is actually a closeup of the witches' broom on C.o. 'Gracilis'. The green fan-shaped foliage is typical of the rest of this plant. The combination of foliage textures & coloring in the witches' broom is quite beautiful! C.o. 'Split Rock' was taken from this witches' broom on C.o. 'Gracilis' before it came to USNA. Don & Hazel Smith gave it to USNA along with the Watnong Pine Collection.

Chamaecyparis obtusa 'Kanaamihiba'

Conifers Coming of Age
Chamaecyparis obtusa

above & below: Chamaecyparis obtusa 'Reis Dwarf'

above: Chamaecyparis obtusa 'Spiralis'

above: Chamaecyparis obtusa 'Split Rock'

Chamaecyparis obtusa 'Split Rock' was propagated from the witches broom on the C.o. 'Gracilis' from Watnong Nursery before the plant was donated to the USNA. The original witches' broom is still a healthy part of the C.o. 'Gracilis', and it definitely adds interest to the 'mother' plant.

Chamaecyparis obtusa 'Reis Dwarf' was named for highly respected Plantsman and much-loved pioneering conifer collector, Joe Reis.

Chamaecyparis obtusa **'Repens'** — bright green, finely textured foliage; low, wide-spreading; full sun or partial shade; 3-6"/yr, 18"H/30"W; z5

Chamaecyparis obtusa **'Rigid Dwarf'** — dark green cupped spays of foliage; distinct upright stiff growth habit; full sun or partial shade; 1-3"/yr, 3'H in 25 yrs; z4

Chamaecyparis obtusa **'Sanderi'** — aka *Thuja orientalis* 'Sanderi'; blue-green, open shell-shaped patterned foliage, purple-plum cast in winter; full sun; 2"/yr, 8'H/4'W in 35 yrs; z5

Chamaecyparis obtusa **'Spiralis'** — dark green, cupped shaped, distinctly twisted foliage; extremely slow-growing, stiff upright conical form; full sun; 1-3"/yr, 3'H/1'W; z5 NOTE: Collectors' plant - not too common, but it is available.

Chamaecyparis obtusa **'Split Rock'** — blue-green, mix of juvenile foliage & fan-shaped adult foliage, one of bluest *C.o*; compact pyramidal habit; full sun; 1-3"/yr, 3'H/2'W; z5

Chamaecyparis obtusa **'Tempelhof'** — yellow-green fan-shaped foliage, brownish in winter; broadly conical form; full sun; 8'H/4'W in 35 yrs; z5

Chamaecyparis obtusa **'Tetragona Aurea'** *g— golden yellow fern-like foliage; slow-growing pyramidal growth habit; full sun with plenty of moisture; 6-12"/yr, 5'H/3'W; z5

Chamaecyparis obtusa **'Torulosa'** [tor-u-LOS-uh] *g— rich, dark green twisted thread-like foliage on contorted branchlets; forms a graceful broad cone (H.J. Welch describes it '. . . upright tangled shrub. . .'; partial shade/sun; 1-3"/yr, 3-4'H/3'W, 15'H/6'W in 35 yrs; z5 NOTE: For growth comparison, this specimen was planted at USNA in '58, 9/62 it measured 23"H/27"W.

Chamaecyparis obtusa **'Verdonii'** *g— rich golden color; compact, wide conical form; full sun; ½"/yr; 4'H/3'W in 35 yrs; z4

Chamaecyparis pisifera (species) — Sawara Cypress; scale-like, new foliage is fresh yellow-green, turning dark green; branchlets flattened in horizontal planes on horizontal branches; slender form; fast growing to 150'; z4 Japan NOTE: prefers moist, humid conditions

Chamaecyparis pisifera **'Boulevard'** — Blue Moss Cypress; soft silver-blue foliage; symmetrical, broadly pyramidal; full sun/partial shade; 6-12"/yr, 6'H/3'W, 15'UH; z4 NOTE: withstands pruning

Chamaecyparis pisifera **'Filifera'** — Green Threadleaf Cypress; very fine-textured medium green thread-like foliage; drooping, pendulous branches; dense, broad, pyramidal form; full sun; 10'H&W, 15'H/12'W in 30 yrs; z5

Chamaecyparis pisifera **'Filifera Flava'** — yellow sport of 'Filifera' with same characteristics except sulphur yellow color

Chamaecyparis pisifera **'Filifera Nana'** — light green long, lacy, thread-like foliage creates a weeping effect; dense, rounded form; full sun; ½-1"/yr (faster growth when young), 3'H/3'W in 15 yrs; z5

Chamaecyparis pisifera **'Gold Spangle'** *g— brilliant yellow adult threadlike foliage; short, slightly twisted branches; broad pyramidal form with narrow crown as it matures; partial shade (prone to sun scorch); 4"/yr, 12'H/7'W in 35 yrs; z5

Chamaecyparis pisifera 'Golden Mop' *g— fine-textured, bright gold thread-like foliage; dwarf, mounding habit, forming broad pyramid with rounded crown with maturity; likes full sun, but may burn in some locations (needs sun for best color); 3-4"/yr, 6'H/4'W in 12 yrs; z5

Chamaecyparis pisifera 'Juniperoides Aurea' — fine golden foliage; compact, low dwarf globe; full sun; 15"H&W; z4   NOTE: (per Susan Martin) this is probably *C.p.* 'Plumosa Juniperoides'

Chamaecyparis pisifera 'Monstrosa' *g— blue-green juvenile foliage & medium green adult foliage, the tight juvenile foliage appears in sections separate from the adult foliage sections; adult foliage has juvenile foliage on the inner branchlets, & sends out long, spidery contorted shoots which, from a distance, give it a soft, fluffy, somewhat whimsical appearance; overall growth habit — as long as the new adult foliage is trimmed off periodically — is a slow-growing globe; full sun; adult foliage growth rate is approx. 15"/yr; z5

Chamaecyparis pisifera 'Nana Aureovariegata' — Golden Dwarf Sawara Cypress; light green with very small needles flecked with golden-yellow; fan-shaped spreading branchlets; dense growth; cushion form; full sun; 8"H/12"W; z5

Chamaecyparis obtusa 'Torulosa'

Chamaecyparis pisifera 'Boulevard'

Chamaecyparis pisifera 'Monstrosa'

Chamaecyparis pisifera 'Filifera Flava' with *Pseudotsuga menziesii* 'Densa' left front, and *Acer palmatum* 'Pixie' left back. Both *C. p.* 'Filifera Flava' and *P.m.* 'Densa' are original Gotelli plants, 30+ years old. While *C. p.* 'Filifera Flava' would be considered 'slow-growing', *P.m.* 'Densa' definitely qualifies as 'dwarf'.

'Monstrosa' as in 'Monster'

Chamaecyparis pisifera 'Monstrosa' – The size in Oct. '62 was 12"H/14"W; the size in Oct. '95 was approx. 4'H/W; this is the only dwarf conifer in the Gotelli Collection that is trimmed on a regular basis. When I questioned the reason this was singled out for regular pruning, Susan Martin said, "Do you know what size this would be if we didn't trim it?!! Why do you think it's named 'Monstrosa' — as in 'Monster'?!!" Answer accepted!! This cultivar is a "must see" when you go to the USNA. It really is unusual! It isn't necessarily what you would want in your own yard, but visiting & seeing it in real life is definitely worthwhile!!

Conifers Coming of Age
Chamaecyparis pisifera

Chamaecyparis pisifera 'Gold Spangle'
Photo by Susan Martin

Chamaecyparis pisifera 'Golden Mop'
Photo by Susan Martin

right: *Chamaecyparis pisifera* 'Golden Mop' with *Tsuga canadensis* selection of 'Sargenti' left front, and *Cornus kousa* in center of photo.

Chamaecyparis pisifera 'Plumosa Aurea Compacta' – *above:* normal growth, *below:* reverting growth

NOTE: This particular specimen of *Chamaecyparis pisifera* 'Plumosa Aurea Compacta' is reverting - once it starts reverting, reversion progresses rapidly. In an effort to keep the original specimen true to type, the USNA takes cuttings from a true-to-type section, propagates them, eventually replacing the reverted specimen.

Colors are fresh and vibrant in early spring, *top*, mellowing, becoming deeper as the leaves mature and summer progresses, *bottom*.

This specimen of *Chamaecyparis pisifera* 'Golden Mop' is only 12 yrs old! It measures close to 8'H/6'W. This is the same cultivar often planted in restricted spaces, with expectations that it will <u>stay small</u>. Several cultivars of golden thread cypress have been introduced with much slower growth rates than 'Golden Mop'. If you specifically require slow growth, search out some of the slower growing cultivars.

Chamaecyparis pisifera '**Pygmaea**' *g– see *C.p.* 'Tsukumo'

Chamaecyparis pisifera '**Plumosa Aurea Compacta**' *g– gold colored foliage year round; tight, compact, neat, round form; very slow-growing dwarf; full sun-partial shade; 2'H&W, 5'H&W in 35 yrs; z4

Chamaecyparis pisifera '**Plumosa Compressa**' *g– small, moss like, light yellow to blue-green foliage; densely set branches; neat, rounded, tightly packed little bun; is one of the true dwarf conifers; slightly wider than high; 2-4'/H&W; z5

Chamaecyparis pisifera '**Snow**' – aka *C.p.* 'Nana Mikko'; light grayish-green fern-like foliage in sprays touched snowy white at the tips; rounded pyramidal form; prefers partial shade with some winter protection; 1-2"/yr, 5-6'H&W; z6

***Chamaecyparis pisifera* 'Squarrosa Intermedia'** **g—* Squarrosa Cypress; bright grayish-blue feathery juvenile foliage; forms a neat, compact globe when young; unique, bushy upright form with age; full sun; 36"H/20"W; z5

***Chamaecyparis pisifera* 'Squarrosa Kanaami-Hiba'** — see *C.o.* 'Kanaamihiba'

***Chamaecyparis pisifera* 'Sungold'** — short, gold-tipped, drooping thread-like foliage in summer, turning green-yellow in winter; dwarf, mounding habit; does not burn; full sun; 18-24"H&W; z5 NOTE: (per Susan Martin) new in trade, should see more of it in near future

above: Chamaecyparis pisifera 'Squarrosa Intermedia' – The long juvenile foliage can be trained to give the mature plant an unusual and unique appearance. (Such as twisting, braiding or tying in knots.)

***Chamaecyparis pisifera* 'Tsukumo'**, aka 'Pygmaea' — emerald green, tightly packed fine textured foliage; very dwarf; compact flat-topped form; full sun/partial shade; ½-1"/yr; 18"H/10"W; z5

Chamaecyparis thyoides (species) — White Cedar; green to grey-green finely divided foliage in flattened, irregular sprays held in dense, up curved bunches; wide columnar form, spire like at the tip; native to swampy bottom lands, prefers moist conditions; to 80'; z3 eastern United States

***Chamaecyparis thyoides* 'Andelyensis'** — grey-green adult foliage in fans on upright (ascending) branches with some juvenile foliage; turns bronze-green in winter; very slow-growing upright form; cones freely; 10'H/3-4'W in 35 yrs; z4

***Chamaecyparis thyoides* 'Heatherbun'** — Purple Heather; soft blue-green juvenile foliage, turning a rich plum color in winter; dwarf, mounding globe form; partial shade/sun; 6-12"/yr, 24-30"H&W; z5 NOTE: can be pruned & shaped

Cryptomeria japonica (species) [crip-to-MEER-ee-uh] — Japanese Cedar; mature leaves are stiff, sharp-pointed, four-angled and curved inward, juvenile leaves are sometimes softer; slender pyramidal tree to 150'; Japan (var. *sinensis*, southern China)

***Cryptomeria japonica* 'Bandai-Sugi'** — bright green summer foliage forms irregular congested moss-like clusters with intermittent normal growth, turns bronze in winter; slow-growing compact globe form becoming irregular with age; sun/partial shade; 2-4"/yr, 4'H/3'W; z6

Cryptomeria japonica 'Bandai-Sugi' –

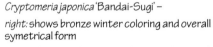

right: shows bronze winter coloring and overall symetrical form

below: shows early spring coloring and general foliage growth pattern

Chamaecyparis pisifera 'Tsukumo' – top: Shows diminutive form. At 30+ years, it only measures about 2½' tall and wide. It does have a tendency to send out reversions, so some prudent pruning is necessary. middle: shows normal foliage; bottom: shows reversion foliage

Conifers Coming of Age
Cryptomeria japonica

Chamaecyparis thyoides 'Andelyensis'

Cryptomeria japonica 'Enko Sugi'

Cryptomeria japonica 'Globosa Nana' – 2' high & wide – *below*: late winter foliage

***Cryptomeria japonica* 'Elegans Nana'** – juvenile foliage is bluish-green in summer, plum colored in winter; very compact, flat-topped globe form; both short and long annual growth that is occasionally delicately curved; partial shade/sun; 6'H/W in 35 yrs; z5

***Cryptomeria japonica* 'Enko Sugi'** – deep green branchlets are long & spidery; form is irregular, broadly pyramidal giving an overall airy & unkept appearance; full sun/partial shade; 6"/yr, 12'H/6'W in 35 yrs; z6

***Cryptomeria japonica* 'Globosa Nana'** – rich green flexible foliage to the ground; dense branches with drooping tips; dense, broad, rounded form; reaches a spread equal or greater than its height; partial shade or sun; 5-10'H&W in 35 yrs; z6

***Cryptomeria japonica* 'Ogon-Sugi'** – long, drooping branchlets on horizontal branches; broad pyramidal form; full sun; 18'H/12'W in 35 yrs; z6

***Cryptomeria japonica* 'Jindai-sugi'** – rich green congested foliage; compact with erect and spreading branches; 2-4"/yr, 5'H/2'W; z6

Cryptomeria japonica 'Ogon-Sugi'

***Cryptomeria japonica* 'Pygmaea'** – dense, rich green short needles, with muddy winter color; compact globose form; partial shade or sun; 18"H/18"W; z5

***Cryptomeria japonica* 'Spiralis'** – aka C.j. 'Kusuri-sugi', 'Granny's Ringlets'; foliage twists spirally around rope-like branchlets; broadly pyramidal form; partial shade; 15"H/24"W, can reach 10'H/5'W in 20 yrs; z5

***Cryptomeria japonica* 'Spiraliter Falcata'** – aka C.j. 'Yore-sugi'; light green foliage curled on twisting golden thin branches, brown-golden where exposed to winter elements, otherwise retains light green coloring; rounded, spreading form; sun/partial shade; 20/24"H&W, 4'H&W in 35 yrs; z5

***Cryptomeria japonica* 'Vilmoriniana'** – rich green short needles summer; bronze winter; very dwarf, irregular, dense globe form; sun/partial shade; 18-24"H&W; z6

> These photos of *Cryptomeria japonica* 'Enko Sugi' and *C.j.* 'Spiraliter Falcata' show similarities in foliage. To see the plants, there are more differences than similarities – *C.j.* 'Enko Sugi' is a fairly large tree, very open, airy (unkept is a good word here), with its long, spidery foliage going every which way. Whereas *C.j.* 'Spiraliter Falcata' has fairly compact foliage on a dense (by comparison!), rounded form.

Cryptomeria japonica 'Spiraliter Falcata' – normal, most-the-year-round foliage,

Cryptomeria japonica 'Spiraliter Falcata' – foliage exposed to winter weather

Cryptomeria japonica 'Yoshino' f. **Bergman** *g— nka *C.j.* 'Yoshino'; foliage is spirally arranged, stiff & harsh to the touch (but looks soft & fluffy from a distance!); whorled and spreading branches sweeping to the ground; mature trees retain branches at or near the ground; reddish-brown fibrous bark peels off in long ribbon-like strips; fast-growing, upright pyramidal form; full sun; 8-10"/yr, 49'H/ 8-10'W in 45 yrs; z6

> ### *Cryptomeria japonica* 'Yoshino' f. Bergman
>
> This is not a Gotelli contribution. This specimen was 18" tall in 1959 when it came to USNA from Rariflora Nursery – at 45+ years, it's close to 50'H/ 10'W. The 'f. Bergman' is for Fred Berman, a widely respected nursery-man from Rariflora Nursery, PA, who died in 1978, and is an optional addition to the botanical name. The USNA distributed this cultivar — all 'Yoshino' came from this original source plant.
>
> It is located against the deciduous woods, on the southern (up the hill) end of the 'Best of Beds', the section of plantings on the east side of Conifer Road, directly across from the entrance to the Gotelli Collection.

X Cupressocyparis leylandii 'Golconda'

below: *Cupressus glabra* 'Blue Ice'

X Cupressocyparis leylandii — Leyland Cypress; natural hybrid between Nootka Cypress (*Chamaecyparis nootkatensis*) and Monterey Cypress (*Cupressus macrocarpa*); combines rapid growth of Monterey Cypress with hardiness and graceful habit of Nootka Cypress; dense, broad columnar form; 12-18"/yr, 65'+ at maturity; not reliably hardy; z5

X Cupressocyparis leylandii 'Naylor's Blue' *g— fans of blue-grey scale-like foliage; tall, pyramidal form to 50'; z5

X Cupressocyparis leylandii 'Golconda' — bright golden lacy foliage; tall pyramidal form; burns slightly in winter; sun/partial shade; 16-20'H/5-7'W; z6

Cupressus glabra (species) — Smooth Arizona Cypress; fine glaucous blue-grey foliage in upward sprays on orange-brown shoots; as it matures, smooth dark-reddish to purple bark blisters, forming circular scales which are shed, leaving pale yellow & dark red patches; broad conical form; 13'H/6'W, 45-60'/UH; z6 Arizona

Cupressus glabra 'Blue Ice' *g— year-round intense silver-blue, fine-textured leathery foliage (looks 'feathery' from distance); bright blue cones; mahogany stems; upright conical habit; full sun; 12-24"/yr, 15'H/8'W; z5

> NOTE: You will want to choose male *Ginkgo biloba* cultivars as the fruit of the female *Ginkgo* produces a noxious odor. After it drops on the ground, as people get near it, you will see them inspecting the bottoms of their shoes… On the other hand, it usually takes 10+ years to produce fruit, so it will take quite awhile before you discover if there's been a mistake!

Ginkgo biloba

Ginkgo biloba (species) [gink-GO—silver apricot—bi-LO-ba—two-lobed (leaves)]— Maidenhair Tree; fan-shaped deciduous leaves, lime-green when they first emerge in spring, medium green through summer, then turning yellow to gold in fall, leaves seem to fall almost all at once, carpeting the ground; ascending branches forming an oval, upright symmetrical form; full sun; 3'/yr when young, 8"/yr as it ages; z3 China

> ### *Ginkgo biloba*
>
> It is considered a living fossil, a survivor of the ice ages. There is evidence of its foliage in ancient fossiles. It is extremely hardy (It's proved that!), tolerates diverse growing conditions, and is disease & pest resistant. It is often used along city streets because of how well it tolerates pollution.

Ginkgo biloba 'Magyar' — selection of grafted male with a uniform upright branching habit, otherwise similar to species; full sun; 50-60'/UH; z4

Glyptostrobus lineatus (species) [glip-to-STRO-bus lin-ee-A-tus] *g— Canton Water Pine; glaucous foliage turns rusty red before falling in autumn; open, sparse narrow pyramidal growth pattern; natural limbing up, with branches

Glyptostrobus lineatus – for fun!
It's the tall wispy tree in the middle. It isn't readily available yet, but if you _really_ want it, it can be found.

Juniperus

Among the most widely used conifers for gardens because of its generally small native sizes. Generally prickly foliage distinguishes it from similar appearing specimens of Chamaecyparis, which are soft to the touch.

Juniperus chinensis 'Aurea'

Juniperus chinensis 'Shimpaku' – Used more for Bonsai. You are more likely to find it through Bonsai sources.

starting 6-8' up on a 12-15' specimen; closely resembles Swamp Cypress (*Taxodium distinchum*); grows in or near water; 15"/yr, 12'H/8'W; requires mild climate; z7 southeast China

Juniperus (genus)[joo-NIP-er-us] – Juniper; about 50 different species in the Northern Hemisphere; two types of foliage – fine & sharply pointed (juvenile), the other flat & scale-like, hugging the stem (adult); in some species & varieties, the spine-like leaves remain throughout life, while in others, the scale-like leaves are dominant; often both types are present; the berry-like structure of the cone distinguishes the junipers; many species are dioecious, i.e. the male & female flowers are carried on separate trees; forms vary from prostrate ground covers, large & small shrubs to small trees; more tolerant of various soil conditions than most conifers; generally quite hardy.

Juniperus chinensis (species) – Chinese Juniper; both adult & juvenile grey-green foliage; slender branchlets on ascending branches; columnar or pyramidal form; to 60'; z3 China, Japan, Mongolia

Juniperus chinensis 'Aurea' – Young's Golden Chinese Juniper; prickly clear yellow juvenile foliage & yellow-gold adult foliage; dense, narrowly conical form; full sun; 3-6"/yr, 15' at maturity; z4

Juniperus chinensis 'Blaauw' – aka J. X media 'Blaauw' (Krussman); rich blue-green foliage of rugged appearance; upright, tight vase form; compact columnar with branches turning outward at the tips; full sun; 4-6'H/3-4'W; z4 NOTE: spider-mite catcher in dry summers! – hosing w/water helps –

Juniperus chinensis 'Kaizuka' – Hollywood Juniper; rich green, scale-like foliage, quite smooth to the touch, retains vivid color all year; upright growth with slightly twisted branches; full sun; 8-16"/yr, 10-30'H/6-8'W; z5

Juniperus chinensis 'Old Gold' – see Juniperus x media 'Old Gold'

Juniperus chinensis 'Shimpaku' – dull dark green foliage, short branches with tufts of scale-like foliage; vase form; sun; 3'H/5W, 5'H/10W in 25 yrs; z5

Juniperus communis (species) – Common Juniper; yellowish-green to grayish-green spine-like leaves; appears both as a shrub and as a narrow tree to 40'; ½" berries used medicinally & for flavorings; z3 Europe, northeastern Asia & North America

Juniperus communis '**Berkshire**' — tiny dark green awl-shaped needles with silvery underside; bronze winter color; low, broad mound form; very slow-growing; full sun; 9-12"H/12-15"W; z4

Juniperus communis '**Echiniformis**' *g— Hedgehog Juniper, aka 'Hemispherica'; tiny 1/8" long, extremely tight, prickly foliage forms gentle mounds as it matures; very dwarf; full sun; 1/4"/yr, 9"H&W, 10"H/2-3' in 35 yrs; z4

Juniperus communis '**Effusa**' — new cinnamon foliage matures to blue-green; soft overlapping branches form a prostrate mat; center slowly builds with new growth forming a shallow mound; sun to deep shade; 12-16"H/4-5'W; z3

Juniperus communis 'Echiniformis'
– above & left –
Look for this special plant in the early planting photos in the History chapter of this book. It is one of the original Gotelli Collection, and wears its age beautifully! It is a wonderful specimen, and invites touching, appearing so soft with its fine-textured foliage & gently lumping, draped form. But it has got to be the very most prickly plant outside the cactus kingdom that I've ever touched! So be fore-warned!

Juniperus communis '**Hemisphaerica**' — see *J.c.* 'Echiniformis'

Juniperus communis '**Pencil Point**' — soft green needles with silver blue striations; narrow columnar form; full sun; 3-6"/yr, 4-5'H/9-12"W; z3

Juniperus conferta (species) — Shore Juniper; prickly, pale green needle-like foliage; stems slightly ascending; dense, creeping prostrate form; z5 sand dunes & coastal areas of Japan

Juniperus conferta '**Silver Mist**' — silvery blue prickly foliage; prostrate form; full sun; 3-6"/yr, 18"H/4'W; z6

Juniperus conferta '**Blue Lagoon**' — bluish-green color with single white band on each needle, beautiful plum winter color; branches are dense & congested; compact, low-growing habit, forming dense, tight mat at maturity; full sun; 6"/UH, 8-10"/W/yr; z5

Juniperus davurica (species) — Dahurian Juniper; fine juvenile foliage mixed with adult foliage; ascending branchlets held on sturdy spreading branches; trailing shrub form; z4 northern Asia

Juniperus davurica '**Expansa Variegata**' — Variegated Juniper; rich blue-green foliage with contrasting splashes of nearly white; stems of adult foliage project from clusters of finer juvenile foliage; mounding, low-spreading form; white variegation sometimes subject to winter damage—needs protection; partial sun; 24"H/5'W in 20 yrs; z5

Juniperus conferta
'Blue Lagoon'

above & below – This USNA introduction was released in 1992. It was discovered in Japan in 1976 during a USNA collecting trip. The plant was under cultivation in the Aritaki Arboretum, where the USNA obtained cuttings. An important highlight: It has shown immunity to rodent damage.

Photo below courtesy of USNA

Juniperus davurica 'Expansa Variegata'

right: *Juniperus davurica* 'Expansa Variegata' – It's medium-small size makes it a good choice to tie in intermediate & low plants

Conifers Coming of Age
Juniperus horizontalis

above: *Juniperus horizontalis* 'Bar Harbor';
Thuja occidentalis 'Wareana Lutescens'
on the right; and
Picea pungens 'Glauca Pendula',
grown on a standard, on the left.

Juniperus horizontalis 'Douglasii' – winter

Juniperus horizontalis (species) — Creeping Juniper; blue-green to glaucous blue leaves, scale leaves dominant; main branches extremely long, prostrate, dense branchlets ascending or erect; trailing form; z4 southern Canada & northern U.S. west to Montana

Juniperus horizontalis '**Bar Harbor**' *g— soft steel-blue foliage turns silvery-plum in winter; ascending branch tips; low creeping branches root to the ground; forms dense mat; full sun; 15"/yr, 10-12"H/7-8'W; z3

Juniperus horizontalis '**Blue Chip**' — compact, silver-blue foliage all year; prostrate, mounding ground cover; 8-10"H/5-6'W; full sun; z4

Juniperus horizontalis '**Blue Forest**' — blue-green foliage, branch tips turn up giving it the appearance of a miniature forest; spreading prostrate form; full sun to partial shade; 12-15"/yr; z4

Juniperus horizontalis '**Douglasii**' — Waukegan Juniper; greyish blue-green mostly scalelike foliage turns a rich purplish-blue in winter; crowded sprays of foliage form upward-reaching branchlets on creeping horizontal branches; spreading, mat-forming, prostrate form; full sun/partial shade; 15"/yr, 6-12"H; z4

Juniperus horizontalis '**Mother Lode**' — rich gold foliage, turning yellow-bronze in winter; prostrate ground cover or draping over wall; full sun to partial shade; 2-3"H; z3

Juniperus horizontalis '**Prince of Wales**' — forms a dense, soft-looking carpet of bright green foliage with waxy, bluish blooms tinged purplish-brown in winter; 4-6"H/6-12'W; z3

Juniperus horizontalis '**Wiltonii**' *g— Blue Rug Juniper; intense silvery-blue foliage, light purplish coloration in winter; young plants send out long lengths of spindly foliage which fill in as the plant matures; prostrate, flat-to-the-ground, forming a solid, slightly mounding, but extremely low mat; effective when allowed to drape over walls, or makes an excellent ground cover; 5-10"H/6-8'W; z3 | Blue Rug Juniper is the MOST common garden juniper.

Juniperus x media 'Plumosa Aurea' – Spring

The seasonal changes in color and the pleasing plume-like branches on its broadly vase-like form make this specimen a highlight in any garden. Coupled with the low maintenance required, this plant is a delight!

...and its not nearly as prickly as most junipers. A definite plus!

Juniperus x media (species) — hybrid of *Juniperus chinensis x Juniperus sabina*

Juniperus x media '**Fairview**' *g— aka *J. chinensis* 'Fairview' & *J.c.* 'Hetz Columnaris'; bright green foliage; wide columnar form; full sun; 6"/yr, 15'H/5'W in 30 yrs; z4

Juniperus x media 'Old Gold' — dwarf form of Gold Pfitzer Juniper; soft, thin, scale-like needles on lacy foliage; new growth is golden yellow; lacy, mounding form; full sun/partial shade; 2-3'H/5'W; z4 NOTE: nice, reliable <u>dwarf</u>

Juniperus x media 'Plumosa Aurea' *g— striking golden-yellow foliage, turning golden-bronze in winter, mostly adult foliage; arching, plume-like branches, with slightly nodding tips; spreading irregular vase form; sun; slow-growing until well established; 3-6"/yr, 3'H/W, 5'H/8'W in 20 yrs; z5

Juniperus x media '**Saybrook Gold**' — new bright yellow juvenile foliage is soft to touch, color deepening to a vivid yellow, becoming prickly as seasons progress; maintains vivid color throughout winter; slightly arching horizontal branches with graceful descending tips; low spreading form, with a bird's nest-like depression in center when viewed from above; 8-10"/yr; 2-3'H/4'W; z4 NOTE: needs full sun to bring out best color

Juniperus x media '**Sulphur Spray**' — bright, sulphur yellow; upward spreading frond-like branches; semi-prostrate form; full sun; 3-4'H/5-6'W; z4

Juniperus procumbens (species) — Japanese Garden Juniper; bluish-green spine-like foliage; ascending branch tips on fast & low-growing, wide-spreading ground cover; 12"H/20'W in 30 yrs; z4 Japan

Juniperus procumbens '**Nana**' *g— Dwarf Japanese Garden Juniper; light bluish-green awl-formed (friendly reminder — 'awl-formed', as in 'needle-sharp') foliage becomes slightly purplish in winter; ground-hugging spreader forming a compact cushion of layered branches; tips of branches turn up; full sun; 12"H/4-6'W; z5

Juniperus procumbens 'Nana'

Especially interesting when staked. It is often used on top of rock walls, allowing it to cascade down the face. It is also widely used as a beginner's Bonsai.

The photo below is taken at the entrace to the Morrison Azalea Garden. It is an exceptionally effective ground cover — The Gotelli Collection has 9 plants used as ground covers — but no walls. To show it off, I thought it needed a wall.

Juniperus x media 'Plumosa Aurea' — Winter

Provides outstanding spots of gold in the landscape — sparkling like beckoning jewels in the distance.

The flash of gold seen in many of the group photos in this book is most often *J. x m.* 'Plumosa Aurea'.

Conifers Coming of Age
Juniperus rigida

above: Juniperus virginiana (species), center with Picea pungens 'Foxtail', left
below: Juniperus virginiana 'Grey Owl'
bottom: Juniperus virginiana 'Nova'

Juniperus rigida (species) – Stiff Needle Juniper, Temple Juniper; bright green, extremely sharp needles; graceful, drooping habit; irregular bush form; 6'H/3'W; z5 Japan

Juniperus rigida 'Pendula' – rigid, awl formed, very sharp needles; quite graceful with long pendulous blue-green branchlets 'hanging like a mane'; full sun; 4-6"/yr, 30-40'/UH; z5

Juniperus sabina (species) – Savin Juniper; green or grey mostly adult foliage; low, arched branches with stems usually upright; spreading form; noted for the scent of its foliage when crushed; 6-8'/UW; z4 central & southern Europe, east to Siberia

Juniperus sabina 'Skandia' *g– pale gray-green feathery foliage; prostrate spreading habit; full sun; 12"H/6'W; z3

Juniperus scopulorum (species) – Rocky Mountain Juniper; grey-green to dark green scale-like foliage; spreading, ascending and/or drooping branches; form varies from open bush to pyramidal; monoecious, i.e. male & female cones on same plant; 30-35'/UH; z5 Rocky Mountains, from Canada, through U.S. & into Mexico

Juniperus scopulorum 'Witchita Blue – bright steel-blue foliage remains bright all year; wide pyramidal form; full sun; 6-12"/yr, 10-15'H/4-6'W, 15-20'/UH; z3 !!!

Juniperus squamata (species) – Flaky or Scaly Juniper; fresh green to bluish green spine-like foliage, silvery white on underside; shrub form varies from sprawling bush to small tree; 'Flaky' is for the flaking of the smooth reddish-brown bark; to 15'; z4 high mountains of Himalayas, China & Formosa

Juniperus squamata 'Blue Star' – irregular dwarf, slow-growing mounding creeper; very dense, steel blue star-shaped foliage; sun with afternoon shade; 2'H/2'W; z4

Juniperus virginiana (species) *g– Eastern Red Cedar, Pencil Cedar (used in making pencils); greenish-grey predominantly adult foliage, with some juvenile type; conical form; full sun; to 90'; z4 eastern North America

Juniperus virginiana

NOTE: Susan Martin said this was a case of looking to the native species to see what would do well at the Arboretum. They weren't sure how well this species would do, but they were having major fungal problems with the scopulorums.

Juniperus virginiana 'Fastigiata' – blue green adult foliage; ascending branches; narrow columnar form; full sun; 12'H/3'W in 30 yrs; z4

Juniperus virginiana 'Grey Owl' *g– Fine, soft, thread-like silvery-grey foliage; medium grower; low, wide spreading habit; 30"H/4-6'W; z5

Juniperus virginiana 'Nova' – medium blue-green foliage; columnar form; full sun; 6"/yr; z4

Larix (genus) – Larch; 10 species; one of the few genera of deciduous conifers; its needle-like foliage is in whorles on short spurs, & is quite similar in appearance to *Cedrus*. One of the first trees to break dormancy in spring, the coloring is of the freshest bright green, turning dark for summer, then with the first frosts of autumn, turning a luminous gold before falling; branchlets are pendulous, not particularly noticeable when young, but after time, forming longer & longer 'streamers' of foliage resulting in a draping effect (more full & lush depending on desirable conditions); branches in whorles, held somewhat upright when young, becoming more and more

ers' of foliage resulting in a draping effect (more full & lush depending on desirable conditions); branches in whorles, held somewhat upright when young, becoming more and more pendulous with age, the upturned branch tips give it a swooping appearance; (*Any hint yet that this is my number one favorite conifer??!*); the small opened cones remain on the branches into much of the winter, giving the long, streaming branchlets a twiggy, knotted appearance (*Quite an awe-inspiring, unforgettable sight if you get to see a mature, healthy larch in winter when it's covered with a light dusting of snow!*); conical form when young, older specimens tend to loose their lower branches, the lower remaining branches becoming more & more outstretched & pendulous, with the top forming a wide, spreading crown.

> The Spring, 1996, *American Conifer Society Bulletin*, Volume 13, Number 2, has several excellent articles featuring *Larix*.

Larix decidua (species) — European or Common Larch; soft, 1-1/2" long fresh green spring foliage, dark green in summer, turning rich golden-yellow before falling; foliage carried singly in dense whorles on side shoots; branches upright when young, more drooping with age & loses lower branches; narrowly conical; to 130'; z2 central & southern Europe NOTE: extremely cold hardy.

Larix decidua 'Pendula' — Weeping European Larch; soft delicate light green needles are a sight to see in early spring!, the summer color is a soft, deep green, turning golden-yellow in fall before dropping; branches arch downward with pendulous branchlets; tall, irregular weeping form; must be staked to desired height; full sun; 4"/yr, H/W depend on training; z3

Metasequoia glyptostroboides (species) [me-ta-se-KWOY-a glip-to-stro-BOY-deez] *g— Dawn Redwood; another deciduous conifer; flattened, soft, feathery, fern-like foliage is bright, light green when it first emerges in spring, becoming dark green in summer, turning a beautiful reddish copper-brown before being shed in autumn; long, somewhat pendulous upswept branches; conical form, becoming broadly conical with age; red-brown bark becomes more prominent with age & base of trunk becomes deeply fissured—buttressed—with age, giving each specimen a unique 'character', each one more interesting & fascinating than the previous specimen!; quite hardy & fast growing in moist, well-drained soil; 13'H/6'W, to 120' at 30 yrs; z4

Metasequoia glyptostroboides 'National' *g— similar in all respects to the species except it is a more narrow form.

Microbiota decussata (species) *g— Siberian Carpet Cypress; rich green fan-shaped fine textured foliage turns slightly bronze in winter; foliage appears soft, lacy, fern-like; low, wide spreading growth habit; prefers shade with well-drained soil, but will grow in sun; exceptionally cold hardy & tolerant of dry conditions; 6-12"/yr, 12"H/3-6'W; z2 Discovered in Siberia in 1921. To see form, refer to description of *Picea pungens* 'Baby Blue Eyes'.

above: Larix decidua 'Pendula'

*below: Microbiota decussata
  – winter foliage   photo courtesy of USNA*

Picea (genus) — Spruce; its appearance is similar to, & often confused with, *Abies* (fir); the sharp foliage is prickly to the touch (thinking of spear for spruce — the spruce's sharp needle points can pierce skin — helps me remember the difference between *Picea & Abies* (Fir-fur); the needles leave sharp protrusions on the stem when removed, leaving it raspy to the touch (*Abies*'s stem is smooth); cones hang downward (*Abies* cones are upright); branches in tiers when young; pyramidal form; found over the entire Northern Hemisphere, usually in mountainous forests.

Conifers Coming of Age
Metasequoia glyptostroboides

Meta sequoia glyptostroboides – Dawn Redwood

above: delicate, fern-like spring foliage

right: early spring

below: Dawn Redwood grove in winter

below right: same grove in spring (This grove is at the fork in the road between the Gotelli, Watnong & Dogwood Collections.)

bottom & next page top: The unique trunks with their deep fisures are much easier to see in the winter.

Although the Dawn Redwood is quite hardy and desease resistant, it is not without problems – Japanese beetles will feed on the green branchlets, rabbits love the bark & deer will use it to rub the velvet off their young antlers!

Metasequoia glyptostroboides - Dawn Redwood
Part of Ancient History

Prior to 1941, the Dawn Redwood was believed to be extinct. In that year a Japanese paleobotanist, using fossil remains, identified it as a separate genus. Also in the same year, a Chinese forester discovered living Dawn Redwoods in eastern Szechwan in China, where the local people called it "water larch". In 1946, an expedition funded by the Arnold Arboretum acquired seeds, then the Arnold Arboretum disbursed them throughout the United States and Europe — with much success. This original seed dispersement has resulted in many magnificent specimens that can be enjoyed today at many arboretums & gardens throughout the world.

Refer to *The American Conifer Society Bulletin*, Volume 4, Number 1, and Volume 13, Number 1, for more information about this unusual tree.

Picea abies (species) — Norway Spruce; 1-1/2" long, dense, dark green needles; branches droop gracefully as plant matures; fastest growing spruce; full sun; 6-8' in 10 yrs, grows to 150'; z3 northern & central Europe

Picea abies –

right: P.a. cultivar in winter (March), with a witch's broom (tight growth foliage in center)

left: same *P.a.*, shows the outline form, with the new spring growth highlighting the tips of the branches – note the gently swooping branches with their up-turned tips & graceful draping foliage – also note that it is a **large** tree

Dawn Redwood or Bald Cypress?

At first glance, Dawn Redwood and bald cypress can be difficult to tell apart. Two key differences to look for:

The green branchlets of Dawn Redwood are placed opposite each other, while those of bald cypress are placed alternately.

The unique differences in trunk form between the two is that bald cypress has a relatively smooth trunk & develops 'knees' as it matures, especially in wet areas; while the base of the trunk of Dawn Redwood continues to broaden & becomes more & more fissured as it ages.

Conifers Coming of Age
Picea abies

above: *Picea abies* cv. – normal growth's flowing form & compact witch's broom, both sparkling with new spring growth
below: *Picea abies* – mature cones

below: *Picea abies* 'Acrocona'

Picea abies 'Acrocona' *g— dark green needles, irregular pendulous habit; abundant cones form on the tips of the branches at a young age; for a short time in early spring, the cones are a strikingly beautiful reddish purple; full sun; 2-3"/yr, 3'H/10'W in 35 yrs; z3

'Acrocona' means with terminal cones on the ends of branches. Known since about 1890, where it was found near Upsala, Sweden, occurring spontaneously in the forest.

Picea abies 'Capitata' — dense dark green needles with tight branches and large buds in clusters; broad conical habit; sun to partial shade; 12'H/12'W in 35 yrs; z4

Picea abies 'Clanbrassiliana' — short, dark green needles and striking brown buds; congested branches grow in layers; multi-stemmed rounded crown; slightly spreading, globose form; full sun; ½-1"/yr, 1'H/12-18"W; z4 NOTES: Prune out course growth as soon as it develops. Reported to be the first dwarf spruce to be grown from witch's broom origin, Lord Clanbrassil's original tree is still alive after nearly two hundred years.

Picea abies 'Clanbrassiliana Stricta' — dense, with dark green needles and ascending branches; narrow conical form; full sun; 3'H/2'H, 10'H/4'W in 35 yrs; z4

Picea abies 'Gregoryana Parsonii' — dense foliage with irregular tufts from variable shoots and clusters result in an uneven mounded form; full sun; 1"/yr, 3'H/3'W; z3 [b7-13"H/23"W 9/19/62]

Picea abies 'Humilis' *g— grey-green, somewhat thickened needles form clusters of congested buds on tightly congested foliage; globose to broadly conical form; ½-1"/yr, 2'H/1'W; z3 Note: Often sends out rigorous shoots that need to be pruned away to maintain miniature form.

Picea abies 'Inversa' — Drooping Norway Spruce; light to mid-green new growth, dark green older foliage; weeping, sprawling branches that if staked, allow the pendulous branchlets to form a long, cascading curtain— totally prostrate if not staked; full sun; 12-14"/yr; z4

Picea abies 'Maxwellii' *g— light green needles radially arranged on stiff, somewhat irregular spreading branchlets; rounded habit, flat top as it matures; very slow growing; full sun; 3'H/4'W in 30 yrs; z4

Picea abies 'Mucronata' — short stiff bright green needles with tan colored terminal buds; ascending branches; dense, broad pyramidal form; full sun; 2"/yr, 28"H&W; z3

Picea abies 'Nidiformis' *g— Bird's Nest Spruce; thin, dark grey-green needles form compact foliage; branches radiate from center, building tight, horizontal layers; depression in middle of flattened globe form — hence the name, 'Bird's Nest'; compact spreading habit; full sun; 2-3"/yr, 1-2'H/3-4'W, 7-8'H/4-5'w in 30 yrs; z3

Picea abies 'Pendula' — Weeping Norway Spruce; dark green needles; will be prostrate unless staked; full sun; 5"/yr, 5'H/4-5'W; z3

Picea abies 'Pendula' – This is just one of the many wonderful specimen that didn't get photographed for this book. All the more reason for you to see the Arboretum for yourself. The P.a. 'Pendula' in bed 11 is outstanding! When Mr. Gotelli acquired it in 1950, it measured 4', and was thought to be 50 years old. It is recorded at 6'H/12'W on 11/2/62.

Charles R. Harrison, *Ornamental Conifers*, has a photo of this specimen in the early '70's, (he lists it as 'Reflexa', but it's the same plant) giving a wonderful description; "…This curiosity in the conifer world seems to have the desire to grow erect but lacks the rigidity and strength to carry out this ambition. The growing tips have an upward-facing tendency, and do not droop until the second year at which stage they evidently lose heart and take on the typical pendulous habit, with just the occasional one or two remaining upright to give the tree a little yearly increase in height. The plant illustrated has quite a strong trunk up to the 1.2m (4ft) level, no doubt having been trained this way when young; from there on it has been left to fend for itself, spreading in all directions, either weeping, spreading or semi-erect. It makes a beautiful specimen if left as a prostrate shrub and grown on a slope or rock ledge, the dark green stiff-looking leaves setting off beautifully the fresh lime-green new spring foliage..."

Thank you, Mr. Harrison! This plant still fits this wonderful description perfectly — even after 25 years!

Picea abies 'Prostrata' — light, mid-green summer foliage, darkening in autumn; wide-spread, mounding in layers with age; 12-18"H/4-5'W; z3

Picea abies 'Pseudoprostrata' — broad, shrubby branches spreading near ground; full sun; 3'H/5'W in 35 yrs; z3

Picea abies 'Pumila' — soft, short, dark-green shiny foliage; rounded, broad globe form; full sun; 3'H/4'W; z3

Picea abies 'Pygmaea' — bright green needles on dense ascending branches; irregular tufts of growth; small, broadly pyramidal form; full sun; 3/4"/yr, 8-12"H/6-8"W, 3'H/5'W in 35 yrs; z3

Picea abies 'Remontii' — bright green needles; broadly conical form with ascending branches; full sun; 3'H/2'W; z3

Picea abies 'Repens' *g — dark green foliage on wide-spreading branches; low, round, slightly mounded prostrate form; tips grow at 45 degree angle; full sun; 3-4"/yr, 2'H/3'W; z3

Picea abies 'Tabuliformis' — Trailing Norway Spruce; tips droop; flat, horizontal branches, low-spreading prostate form, mounding with age; full sun; 1"/yr; z3

Picea bicolor (species) — Alcock's Spruce, fka *Picea alcockiana*; needles range from green to bluish green above, bright silver beneath; gray to gray-brown peeling bark; large, pyramidal form, becoming open & gaunt with age; full sun; 40-50' in 30 yrs; z6 Japan

Picea bicolor 'Howells Dwarf' *g — bicolor needles, appearing blue-green from a distance; ascending branches; broad spreading form, lacking a defined terminal; full sun; 3"/yr, 6'H/4'W; z4

Picea glauca (species) — White or Canadian Spruce; greyish-green to bluish-green ½" long needles; spreading or ascending branches; pyramidal form; 4-6"/yr, 6'H/30"W, 75-100'/UH; z2 Canada & northern U.S.

Picea glauca 'Conica' — Dwarf Alberta Spruce; compact, very symmetrical pyramidal form; soft, thin, grass-green needles radiate around the stem; prefers moist, well-drained soils and good air circulation; full sun, tolerates partial shade; 2"/yr; 3'H/2"W; z2 NOTE: Wide variation in growth rates, individual specimens vary & growing conditions vary; monitor overall growth, watching for areas where growth spurts much faster than overall tree (reversions) — prune out.

Picea glauca 'Wild Acres' — small grey-green needles; flat-topped compact form; full sun; 3'H/2'W; z2

Picea glehnii (species) *g — Saghalin Spruce; blue-green foliage; tall tree with exfoliating, chocolate brown bark; full sun; 8'H/3'W; z4 Japan and Manchuria

Picea abies 'Nidiformis' – above center, with *Juniperus virginiana* towering in the background, is close to 35 years old. It is nearly 8'H/5'W, and is still quite dwarf compared to the *P.a.* species – This mature height is much larger than what most people have in mind when they purchase a 1'/H Bird's Nest Spruce.

It grows faster as young plant, but growth rate slows as it matures. It is not uncommon for this particular cultivar to outgrow its allotted space because it doesn't stay small.

P.a. 'Oldhamiana' is the large shrub on the left, with *P.a.* 'Pseudoprostrata' in front, extending itself to the left.

below: *Picea bicolor* – This dramatic coloring in the cones only happens for a very short period in the early spring.

Conifers Coming of Age
Picea mariana

above: Picea omorika 'Nana' – March & April
(...spring is just around the corner)

below: Picea omorika 'Pendula'

Picea mariana (species) — Black Spruce; bluish-green above & bluish white on stomata bands below, ½" long needles; irregular, somewhat pendulous branches; generally pyramidal form, varies in wild, depending on altitude, from tall tree to small, stunted bushes; 60-100'/UH; z2 Canada, northeastern United States

Picea mariana **'Nana'** *g— Blue Nest Spruce; small, thin needles; tips of new spring foliage are blue-green, turning to gray-green by late summer; forms a compact small mound with a nest-like depression; one of the most dwarf of the spruces; full sun; 1"/yr, 14"H/24"W; z3

Picea maximowiczii (species) — Japanese Bush Spruce; shiny dark green needles; densely crowned tree with very resinous buds; 3'H/3'W; z4 Japan

> NOTE: Considered a rare species, but should become more readily available.

Picea omorika (species) — Serbian Spruce; foliage is shiny deep green above, silver underneath, giving a bi-color effect; pendant branches curve upwards at the ends; cones deep purple when young; slender, extremely narrow form (narrowly conical) gives a graceful, spire-like appearance; 15"/yr, 100'/UH; z4 Yugoslavia, confined to a small area on limestone slopes at altitudes 2,500-6,000'

Picea omorika **'Gnom'** — aka *P. x mariorika* 'Gnom'; short, blue-green needles; small, somewhat irregular, globose form; full sun; 1-2"/yr; z4

Picea omorika **'Nana'** — flattened needles with a bluish-green bicolor effect; irregular, compact, wide conical form; full sun; 3'H/2'W; z3

Picea omorika **'Pendula'** *g— bluish-green bicolored foliage; graceful downward-hanging branches that turn up at the tips; narrow columnar form; sensitive to drought; full sun; 10-12"/yr, 10'H/3'W, 30'H/4'W in 35 yrs; z4

> Larry Stanley, owner of Stanley & Sons, describes the form perfectly, "...has the look of a tree laden with snow."

Picea orientalis (species) — Oriental Spruce; lustrous dark green foliage only 1/4 to 1/3" long; colorful coning, it is quite a show when masses of bright red male cones appear in early spring; dense branches to the ground, upturning at the ends; handsome full pyramidal form; 12"/yr, 200'UH; z4 Caucasus and northern Asia Minor

Picea orientalis **'Gowdy'** *g— small rich-green glossy needles; striking in spring when pale green new growth is set off by dark green older foliage; pyramidal form with recurved, sweeping branches; full sun; slow-growing, 15'H/10'W in 45 yrs; z4 NOTE: Gotelli purchased in 1950 at 3'H

Picea orientalis **'Gracilis'** — dark green foliage; dense, conical form; full sun; 8'H/4'W; z4

Picea orientalis **'Nana'** — dense, light green foliage; compact globose form; 1-3"/yr; full sun; z4

Picea orientalis **'Skylands'** — aka *P.o.* 'Aurea Compacta' golden yellow when young; interior dark green as it matures, contrasting against new golden growth; prefers partial shade when young; rich yellow-green foliage when grown in partial shade; beautiful red cones in early spring; slow-growing pyramidal form; 6-12"/yr, 4'H/3'W; z4

Picea pungens (species) [*pungens*—sharp] — Colorado or Blue Spruce, fka *Abies menziesii*; dark bluish-green to bluish-grey, 1" long, slightly curved, thick, rigid & prickly foliage arranged all around the stem (*radially*); straight

zontal branching contributes to its regal appearance; full, symmetrical pyramidal form, with branches to the ground in favorable conditions; 10'H/ 5'W, 100-150'/UH; z2

> *Picea pungens* – Comes from dry, hot sites at high altitudes in the southern end of the U.S. Rocky Mountains. It does not tolerate wet feet or temperate climates.
>
> The collective name of *Picea pungens glauca* is given to the natural occurring blue variety – some specimens loose the blue coloring as they mature; the majority of blue cultivars are propagated vegetatively to ensure consistent coloring.
>
> Prone to attacks of spider mites & aphids.

Picea pungens '**Baby Blueyes**' – bright blue foliage; dense, symmetrical, pyramidal form; full sun; 3-5"/yr; z3

Picea pungens '**Compacta**' *g– long, bright blue, sharp-tipped needles; compact & densely branched, flat-topped form; with maturity, its lower horizontal branches form a beautiful, graceful spreading skirt; full sun; 2'H/2'W; z3

Picea pungens '**Fat Albert**' – dense blue foliage; full, symmetrical conical form; full sun; 8'H/2'W; z2

Picea pungens '**Glauca**' – see *P.p.* (species)

Picea pungens '**Glauca Pendula**' – bright silvery-blue color in early spring and summer; weeping or creeping, depending on training, irregular form, even when staked; branches become more pendulous as it matures; full sun; stake to desired height, 6-8"/yr; z3

> *Picea pungens* 'Glauca Pendula' – There is an excellent photo from the other side of this specimen in Robert A. Obrizok's book, *A Garden of Conifers*. He features the Gotelli Collection & his own collection. If you've enjoyed this book, you will enjoy his. In fact, his would be a natural next step for many folks once they've been bitten by the 'conifer bug'. Taking a quote from a spot well into his book:
>
> "**Proceed with caution!** The combinations of colors, sizes, and foliage textures within a garden of conifers is infinite. The collecting of dwarf conifers often begins innocently with a few plants. Soon your garden will contain a dozen or two. After nineteen years or so, you might have as many as 450 conifers. A transformation occurs: you once purchased plants for the landscape, now you landscape for the plants. It can happen. It did—to me."

Picea orientalis 'Nana'

Picea orientalis 'Skylands'
photo by Susan Martin

Picea pungens 'Baby Blueyes' – Introduced in 1986 by D&H Nursery. See the ACS Bulletin, Vol. 4, No. 4, about the introduction of a new cultivar, including the patenting process. It was a 25-year process! (*Microbiota decussata* is on both sides)

> **_Picea pungens_ 'Glauca Pendula'**
>
> This specimen has character!
>
> O.K. – now, stand back & squint your eyes just a bit... With a bit of imagination (quite a bit), doesn't this look like a looming, 3-4 -armed shaggy creature, stooped-shouldered (but friendly, with his obvious effort at a grin...), slowly trudging towards you, trying to give a welcoming bow – and with that little extra string of dangling foliage on his right that just might be needed as a prop for that heavy outstretched arm(s)???
>
> Too much? What do you see? You must agree it is unique!

Conifers Coming of Age
Picea pungens

right: *Picea pungens 'Glauca Prostrata'*

below: *Picea pungens 'Hoopsii'* – spring
photo courtesy of USNA

***Picea pungens* 'Glauca Prostrata'** aka *P.p.* 'Glauca Procumbens' — frosty-blue foliage; spreading form hugs the ground; full sun; 6-12"/yr, 12-18"H/5-6'W; z3

***Picea pungens* 'Hoopsii'** — *g— dense, bright, silver-blue foliage, considered one of the bluest of spruce; for a very short time when the large, pendulous cones first emerge in the spring, they are a striking magenta/purple — an amazing contrast against the silver-blue foliage; lacks strong leader when young, giving it an irregular form, but becoming a stately pyramidal form with maturity; full sun; 6-12"/yr, 8'H/3'W, 18-20'H in 35 yrs, 30'-50'/UH; z3

below: *Picea pungens 'Hoopsii'* – summer
Chamaecyparis pisifera 'Monstrosa' is the feathery form in front/left – the flash of orange is butterfly weed (*Asclepias tuberosa*).

photo by Susan Martin

above: *Picea abies 'Pygmaea'* (left front), *Picea pungens 'Hoopsii'* (center), *Thuja occidentalis 'Wareana Lutescens'* (far right), *Juniperus 'Parsonii'* (front), all original Gotelli collection plants. The dome-shaped foliage to the right of *P.p.* 'Hoopsii' is butterfly weed. The photo above was taken Spring-1981, while the photo on the left is Summer-1993. The two photos provide an unusual visual comparison of a mature *P.p.*'Hoopsii' at 20+ years and 30+ years.

When Gotelli obtained *Picea pungens 'Hoopsii'* from Montreal Botanical Gardens in 1960 it was 12"/H; March 1962 it was 37"H/40"W; 1995, at 35 years old, it measures close to 20'/H.

Picea pungens '**Hunnewelliana**' — silvery-blue foliage; slow-growing, semi-dwarf conical form; full sun; 3'H/4'W in 30 yrs; z2 NOTE: 8/28/62 it measured 5"H/8"W

Picea pungens '**Foxtail**' — good blue color; branchlets have tapered needle formation resembling fox tails; pyramidal form with open, bushy growth pattern with somewhat twisted branches; full sun; 4-6"/yr, 10'H/4-5'W; z3 NOTE: fox tail form is more obvious on specimens grown in the West

Picea pungens '**Kosteri**' — steel-blue foliage; branches angle upwards; somewhat irregular pyramidal form; full sun; 8-12"/y, 6-8'H/4-5W; z3 NOTE: pruning often necessary to maintain pyramidal form

Picea pungens '**Montgomery**' — compact, bright blue foliage; slow growing; broad, somewhat mounding pyramidal form; full sun; 2-3"/yr, 3'H/3'W; z3

Picea pungens 'Montgomery'

Picea pungens '**Pendula**' — see *P.p.* 'Glauca Pendula'

Picea pungens '**Prostrata**' — see *P.p.* 'Glauca Prostrata'

below: Pinus bungeana – This gorgeous specimen is at the entrance to the Morrison Gardens in the Azalea Collections.

Picea pungens '**Blue Mist**' — long blue needles; prostrate form; full sun; 3-6"/yr, 12-18"H/30-36"W; z3

This is one of my very favorites – I was fascinated the first time I saw it! I make a point of visiting it every time I go to the Arboretum.

Pinus (genus) — Pines; approx. 110 species; long needles held in bundles, usually 2, 3 or 5 (rarely 1 or 6-8) needles per bunch, in a sheath at the base of each bundle; usually soft to the touch (see '*Trees of North America and Europe*' by Roger Phillips, for species foliage comparisons); different kinds of pines are primarily distinguished by the number of needles occurring together (see Glossary) (see '*The Trees of North America*' by Alan Mitchell, for more in-depth information presented in an easy-to-understand format). The showing of 'candles' is often dramatic among pines, where the silvery new growth buds elongate, the new needles held tight to the stem, all standing erect, looking like candles. Many drop older needles yearly from 2-3-year growth, others hold needles 5 yrs & more. They generally thrive in poor, well-drained acid soils, and tolerate dry conditions. Except for shrubby mugo pine (*Pinus mugo*) from the Alps, most species are tall trees, and range from Arctic Circle to the equatorial zone.

Pinus bungeana (species) *g— Chinese Lacebark Pine; long, stiff emerald-green needles, 3 to a cluster; open, somewhat sparse branching habit; oval crowned tree, often multi-stemmed; as it matures, large irregular scales exfoliate from branches & trunk(s), revealing a beautiful patchwork of whites, greens & browns; full sun; 6-12"/yr, extremely slow-growing when young, usually only reaching 6' in 10 yrs, eventually reaching 50'; z5

Conifers Coming of Age
Pinus cembra

above & below: Pinus bungeana

Pinus cembra (species) — Swiss Stone Pine; very soft, lustrous blue-green needles in bunches of 5 w/blue-white stomatic lines; needles stay on tree up to 5 yrs; blue cones stay on the tree 2-3 years (but never open); slow-growing compact pyramid to ground level; full sun; 3-6"/yr, 6'H/3'W; 30-40'H/15-25'W/UH; z2 mountains of central Europe; has been cultivated for over 250 yrs

Pinus cembra '**Chalet**' — soft bluish-green foliage; dense, rounded narrow form; full sun; 5-6"/yr, z4

Pinus cembra '**Compacta Glauca**' — dark blue needles; slow, very dense growth habit; full sun; 3-6"/yr, 5-6'H/30-36"W; z4

Pinus cembra '**Pygmaea**' — short, blue-green needles grow in congested tufts; irregular, flat-topped form; sun; 3-4'H/2'W; z3

Pinus contorta (species) — Shore Pine; short, yellowish-green, twisted double needles; large bush to medium sized tree; grows well in light sandy soil; does not tolerate lime soils; 6'H at 10 yrs; z5 coastal form of Lodgepole Pine, from Alaska to Mendocino, California.

Pinus contorta '**Spaans Dwarf**' — short green needles; sturdy, upright branches twist & curve, forming an irregular pyramid; full sun; 3-6"/yr, 3-4'H/2-3'W; z5

Pinus densiflora (species) — Japanese Red Pine; thin, light grass-green 3 to 4-1/2" long needles held in pairs; reddish, exfoliating bark as it matures; irregular broad habit, becoming flat-topped with age, trunk frequently leaning or crooked; 70-100'/UH; Japan

> *P.densiflora – P.thunbergiana* – There are cultivars of both of these species with the same cultivar name. One distinguishing feature to look for is the difference in buds:
> *P.densiflora* has thin, red buds — *P.thunbergiana* has thick, silvery buds.

Pinus densiflora '**Oculus-draconis**' — Dragon's Eye Pine; needles are marked with 2 yellow stripes which are apparent as alternating yellow and green bands; irregular growth pattern; sun; 8-16"/yr, 10'H/5'W, 40-60'/UH; z4

Pinus densiflora '**Pendula**' *g— dark green foliage; reddish-brown bark; pendulous branches if staked, otherwise, forms a dense, creeping carpet; full sun; 8-12"/yr, H/W depend on staking; z4 Japan NOTE: in '60 at 25 yrs it was 2'H/5'W. It was not readily available in this country before '60's.

Pinus densiflora '**Umbraculifera**' *g— aka Tanyosho Pine, Tabletop Pine; long, dark green needles; heavy show of tiny cones; dwarf, dense spreader with flattish parasol-like top; once established has branches dividing from the base; older bark exfoliates, exposing patterns with various shades of reddish brown; full sun; 3-6"/yr, 4-5'H/4-5'W, 15'H/20'W in 30 yrs; z4

Pinus cembra

Pinus densiflora 'Oculus-draconis'
photo courtesy of USNA

Pinus densiflora 'Pendula'

***Pinus x densi-thunbergii* cv. 'Beni Kujaku'** — dragon's-eye type of black pine; variegated (banded) cream and green needles; irregular upright habit; full sun; 12-24"/yr, 8'H/4'W; z5

Pinus flexilis (species) — Limber Pine; smooth, dark green 5-needled foliage; flexible young shoots can be bent, looped and knotted without breaking; needles hold 5-6 years before falling; tall conical form, lower branches die off as it matures; to 60'H; Rocky Mountains from Canada to California & New Mexico.

***Pinus flexilis* 'Glauca'** — Blue Limber Pine; short, curved, silvery-blue foliage; open-branched, wide pyramidal form; full sun; 8'H/3-4'W, 25'/UH; z4

***Pinus flexilis* 'Glenmore'** — grey-green needles; very slow growing; densely pyramidal; sun; 5'x5' in 30 yrs; z4

***Pinus flexilis* 'Pendula' *g**— long blue-green needles; low growing, wide spreading, irregular growth; full sun; 6-12"/yr; z5

***Pinus flexilis* 'Vanderwolf's Pyramid'** — long twisting needles, deep green on top, silver blue underside; dense, ascending branches; large conical form; full sun; 8-16"/yr, 8'H/3'W; z4

right: Pinus flexilis 'Vanderwolf's Pyramid'
below right: Pinus heldreichii var. leucodermis

Pinus heldreichii var. leucodermis (species) — Bosnian Redcone Pine; glossy, dark black-green, stiff needles arranged in pairs, curving slightly inward towards the shoot; grey bark; slow-growing slender pyramidal habit; full sun; 6'H/3'W; 90'/UH; z4 Italy & Balkans

***Pinus heldreichii var. leucodermis* 'Compact Gem'** — lustrous deep green curved needles in dense clusters; compact, slow-growing, broadly pyramidal form; 3-4'H/2-3'W; full sun; z3

Pinus koraiensis (species) — Korean Pine; slender, 4-1/4" long needles in dense clusters of five, outside glossy green, inner surface blue-white, appears blue-green from a distance; thick, flaking dark gray bark; broadly conical form; to 115'/H; z3 river valleys & low mountain slopes of NE Asia, Japan, Korea

***Pinus koraiensis* 'Glauca'** — aka 'Silveray'; long, silvery-green needles; pyramidal form; sun; 6-12"/yr, 15'H/8'W in 25 yrs; z4

Pinus densiflora 'Umbraculifera' —
above top: 'Limbing up' as this specimen matures accentuates the flat-top appearance and the extraordinary exfoliating bark. This cultivar tends to 'limb-up' naturally as it ages because the lower branches get shaded, then die out.

above middle: The contrasts in the exfoliating bark become more pronounced as it matures.

above bottom: Candling on this cultivar is brilliant! Quite a sight to see when it gets 'decorated' each spring!

below:
Pinus x densi-thunbergii cv. 'Beni Kujaku'

Pinus flexilis 'Pendula'

The specimen in bed 22 is only about 6 years old. The original Gotelli plant died in 1982; it measured 12'H/17'W. Susan Martin said that most of the plants in the trade have come from that original Gotelli plant.

It is pretty much standard practice among collectors to propagate their most valuable specimen, then disperse their propagations. It is considered insurance. That way, if anything happens to their original plant, there is still 'true' plant material available.

Plant distribution is an integral part of the Arboretum's purpose. A side benefit is that when a plant dies unexpectedly, they can get a new start from someone who had received starts from the original plant.

Conifers Coming of Age
Pinus mugo

above: Pinus mugo 'Aurea' – winter

below: Pinus mugo 'Mops'

Pinus leucodermis (species) – Bosnian Pine; rigid, 3-1/2" long, pairs of densely clustered, dark green needles, curving inward towards shoot; strong pyramidal form to 80'; z5 Italy & Balkans

Pinus mugo (species) – Dwarf Mountain Pine; pairs of stiff, dark green needles; 4 different geographical races with ranges in size from low, bushy shrubs (varieties *mughus* and *pumilio*) to 30-80' tall trees (varieties *rostrata* and *rotundata*); z2 mountains of central Europe, Balkans & Apennines in Italy.

Pinus mugo 'Aurea' – Gold Mugo Pine; long, twisted, light green needles spring, medium green summer, then turn bright gold in winter; semi-dwarf open bush form; full sun; 3'H,/3'W; z2

Pinus mugo 'Gnom' – deep, jade green foliage; dense, globose form; full sun; 6'H/4'W, 10'H/6W in 35 yrs; z3

Pinus mugo 'Mops' – dark green needles; very compact globose form; full sun; ½-1"/yr, 4'H&'W in 35 yrs; z3

Pinus mugo 'Mops' –

left: P.m. 'Mops' from the original Gotelli Collection (35+ yrs). The next is a propagation from the original, only 8"H/16"W in seven years. Look closely at the bottom photo. That tight growth in the center of the plant is a witch's broom – a dwarf on a dwarf! In this instance, a miniature on a miniature! Quite amazing!

Sour Note: I am sorry to report that you will not be able to see this plant as I did, as it's pictured here. Someone vandalized it – probably trying to take cuttings. When I saw it during my last visit, the tiny witch's broom had been hacked into, damaging it, and destroying its natural wonder and beauty for the rest of us. I won't go into what I think or how I feel about this type of theft and vandalism, except to say it must have been done by an incredibly selfish, greedy individual; a person without love or respect for plants or people.

Pinus mugo 'Oregon Jade' – bright green foliage; compact form; full sun; 2-4"/yr, 3'H&W; z2

Pinus nigra (species) – Austrian Pine; 4-6" long, dark green needles held in pairs; broadly columnar; 150'/UH; z4 central & southern Europe & *Asia Minor.

Pinus nigra 'Globosa' – long, dark green needles; dense, globose form; multi-trunked with age; limbs up naturally as it ages, exposing rich, dark, almost black bark; full sun; 10'H&W in 30 yrs; z4

Pinus nigra 'Hornibrookiana' *g– rich, long dark green needles; brilliant display of cream-colored candles in spring; slow-growing, compact globose mound; full sun; 3-6"/yr, 2'H/3'W; z3

Pinus nigra 'Hornibrookiana'

Pinus palustris (species) – Longleaf yellow pine; slender, 10-15" long needles in bunches of 3; foliage is dark green as it matures, bright green in the 'grass' stage, when it looks more like a fountain of grass than a tree; the long needles droop gracefully from stubby branches; cones grow up to 10" long; irregular crown; 120'/UH; z9 southeast USA from southeast Virginia west to eastern Texas

Pinus parviflora (species) — Japanese White Pine; slightly twisted 2-1/2" long needles in clusters of five, blue-green top with blue-white underside, giving the tree a silvery-blue appearance; retains needles for four years; broadly columnar, slightly irregular form, becoming open & flat-topped with age; slow-growing to 80'H; z5 mountains of Japan

Pinus parviflora **'Adcock's Dwarf'** — short, medium green recurved needles, silver-grey on underside, clustered on branch tips; globose form; full sun; 1-3"/yr, 2'H/2'W; z5

Pinus parviflora **'Al Fordham'** — long, medium green needles, silvery beneath; upright, extremely slow growing; full sun; z5

Pinus parviflora **'Aoi'** — small curved blue-grey needles; tight bunches of foliage along branches; irregular upright habit; full sun; 6-10"/yr, 5'H/3'W; z5

Pinus parviflora **'Baldwin'** — blue-green needles; large pyramidal with open habit; full sun; 2-4"/yr; 12'H/6'W in 25 yrs; z5

Pinus parviflora **'Brevifolia'** — short blue-green needles; ascending branches on compact, upright form; full sun; 6-12"/yr, 8'H/4'W; z5

Pinus parviflora **'Ei-Ko-nishiki'** — short, deep green foliage; corky trunk with age; artistic, irregular branching, almost prostrate form; full sun; 12-18"H/4-6'W; z4

Pinus parviflora **'Gimborns Pyramid'** — intense blue-green foliage; slow-growing broad pyramid; full sun; 4-6"/yr, 4'H/2'W; z5

Pinus parviflora **'Glauca'** — long, twisted blue needles; pyramidal small tree; full sun; 12-16"/yr, 6'H&W; z5

Pinus parviflora **'Glauca Nana'** — short, twisted blue needles; extremely slow-growing with open habit; irregular, upright growth when young, becoming a flat-topped globe; full sun; 3-6"/yr, 2'H/12"W; z5

Pinus parviflora **'Ko-ko-no-e'** *g— dark green, thick, twisted needles; upright irregular habit; full sun; 3-4"/yr; z5

above: Pinus palustris — The long drooping foliage & enormous white buds are distinctive characteristics of this species. It has an extended grass stage which acts as its protection from forest fires. It occurs on dry, barren, sandy soils and must be transplanted when young.

right: Pinus parviflora 'Aoi'
below: Pinus nigra 'Hornibrookiana'

Conifers Coming of Age
Pinus parviflora

Pinus parviflora 'Nana' — curled green & blue needles; upright form; full sun; 3'H&W; z5

Pinus parviflora 'Ogon Janome' — Golden Dragon Eye Pine; bands of distinctive bright golden-yellow on green needles; irregular broad conical form; full sun; 3-6"/yr, 3'H/2'W; z5

Pinus parviflora 'Venus' — short, light grey-blue needles curl around the branches; upright pyramidal habit; full sun; 6'/UH; z3

Pinus parviflora 'Watnong' — medium green foliage; very slow-growing, regular, pyramidal form; sprouts or flushes grow from old wood, giving greater fullness; full sun; 5' in 20 yrs; z5

left: Pinus parviflora 'Ei-Ko-nishiki' – New growth highlights the full, tufty foliage, and tight green cones take shape, contrasting with the mature cones. (one of my very most favorite plants!)

above: Pinus parviflora 'Ei-Ko-nishiki' – This plant is an artform in itself! The snow highlights its unusual outline and form. I had mentioned to Susan F. Martin that there were a few plants that would be outstanding sprinkled with snow. ...And this is one of them!

Pinus pumila (species), [POO-mi-la] — Japanese Stone Pine, Dwarf Siberian Pine; 5-needle pine with fine blue-green foliage; mature plants produce small violet-purplish cones that change to reddish-brown over a two-year period; prostrate shrub to small tree; 2'H in 10 yrs, 10'/UH; z3 high mountains of Japan & east Asia

Pinus resinosa (species) — Red Pine; needles densely packed in pairs, long, straight & brittle (break clean when bent); slender conical form, loosing lower branches with age; to 90'H; south-eastern Canada, the Lake States, & NE United States

Pinus resinosa 'Don Smith' — long, closely set, dark green needles; spectacular spring candles accented with tiny red male cones at the tips; spreading, mounding form with dense, upright branches; full sun; 3'H/4'W; z5

Pinus resinosa 'Don Smith' was named in honor of a much-loved and respected plantsman. Don Smith, together with his wife Hazel, were owners of Watnong Nursery and benefactors of the Watnong Pinetum Collection.

This plant has a beautiful form, and its spring candling display is really worth seeing. When you take a closer look, you will see that many of the long candles actually have a small red 'flame' in the form of a minute male pollen cone at the tip.

Pinus strobus (species) — Eastern White Pine, Weymouth Pine; dark blue-green needles in bunches of five (only 5-needled pine east of the Rockies); narrowly conical; 150'H; z3 eastern North America

Pinus strobus '**Brevifolia**' *g— dark blue-green needles, silvery beneath; upright, extremely compact, pyramidal form; very slow-growing; full sun; 18-24"H/8-12"W; z3

Pinus strobus '**Macopin**' *g— blue-green foliage; slow-growing; open, layered irregular globe form; full sun; 30-36"H&W; z3

Pinus strobus '**Merrimack**' — soft green foliage; dense, compact rounded form; full sun; 3'H&W; z3

Pinus strobus '**Nana**' *g— soft, tufty bunches of blue-green foliage; dense, spreading, irregular mound habit; full sun; 3'H/4'W; 5'H/7'W/UH; z3

Pinus strobus '**Ontario**' *g— both short & long needles; irregular dwarf with layered, spreading habit; part shade-sun; 1"/yr; z3

Pinus strobus '**Pendula**' *g— large clusters of long blue-green needles; twisting, graceful, pendulous branches; needs staking, but best if not staked past 6'; full sun; 6-12"/yr, 12-24"/yr in some areas; H&W depend on training; z3

Pinus strobus '**Prostrata**' — light blue-green needles; sprawling, open habit; branches laying flat on ground or forming slight mound; full sun; 12-24"/yr, 1'H/5-6'W; z4

Pinus strobus '**Pumila**' *g— twisted, silvery green needles; globose habit; full sun; 1-2"/yr, 4'H&W in 30 yrs; z3

Pinus strobus '**Torulosa**' [tor-U-los-uh] *g— long, twisted light green needles; dense, twisting branches; unique open upright form; full sun; 4-6"/yr, 25'H/6'W in 25 yrs; z3

Pinus strobus '**Winter Gold**' *g— fka Hillside Winter Gold; green summer foliage, turning bright yellow-gold in winter; wide, open pyramidal form with somewhat sparse foliage; full sun; 4'H/3'W; z3

Pinus sylvestris (species) — Scots Pine; stiff, twisted, blu-grn needles in pairs; dense pyramidal when young, irregular, broadly spreading form with age; org-red bark becomes more picturesque with age; 80-100'H; z2 Europe

Pinus sylvestris '**Albyns**' *g— thick, shiny, bluish green needles; slow-growing prostrate form; full sun; 14-18"H/4'W; z2

Pinus sylvestris '**Aurea**' — yellow-green needles in spring, bluish-green in summer, turning bright yellow-gold in winter; slow-growing; bushy when young, conical when mature; full sun; 3'H/2'W; z4

Pinus sylvestris '**Beuvronensis**' *g— light blue-green foliage; dense, broad globose bush, flat-topped with age; full sun; 2'H/3'W, 3'H&W/UH; z4

above & below: Pinus strobus 'Macopin'

below: Pinus strobus 'Torulosa'

below: Pinus strobus 'Winter Gold'
It's open, somewhat whispy form along with the brilliant winter gold coloring, combine to give Winter Gold a transluscent appearance – especially emphasized when the sun shines from behind. A great example of winter interest, P.s. 'Winter Gold' provides a stunning focal point in the winter landscape!

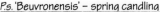
P.s. 'Beuvronensis' – spring candling

P.s. 'Beuvronensis' – winter

Conifers Coming of Age
Pinus sylvestris

above: Pinus sylvestris 'Aurea' with Juniperus horizontalis 'Bar Harbor' – late October. This is a study in dramatic contrasts & great winter interest! The uniform ground-hugging appearance & muted winter coloring of Juniperus horizontalis 'Bar Harbor' forms a perfect contrasting background, allowing the irregular form & brilliant golden coloring of Pinus sylvestris 'Aurea' to completely monopolize this winter show.

left and left/top: Pinus sylvestris 'Aurea' – late March — still winter in Washington, D.C. —And to prove to myself that this brilliant winter color is truly a characteristic of this cultivar, the top foliage photo was taken the following year in late March.

Pinus sylvestris **'Fastigiata'** **g*– long, blue-green needles; orange papery bark as it matures that is exposed by its upright, narrow columnar form; full sun; 8'H/2'W; z3 NOTE: tie branches in winter to prevent snow damage

Pinus sylvestris **'Globosa Viridis'** – long, dark green needles in dense clusters of short branchlets, at the ends of outstretched branches, giving it a 'lumpy' appearance; late in the season, short needles develop & surround the white bud; dense globose form; full sun; 3'H/2'W; z3

right: Pinus sylvestris 'Globosa Viridis' – early March. The light sprinkling of snow emphasizes the dense clustering of the branchlets.

below: Pinus sylvestris 'Hillside' (Creeper) – October 1980, soon after it was planted.   *photo by Susan Martin*

above: Pinus sylvestris 'Hillside' (Creeper) – This beautiful specimen died after being stressed from the 1995 drought. For the next few years, the plant you see in its place will look more like the 1980 plant shown on the opposite page/bottom.

above: Pinus sylvestris 'Hillside' (Creeper)

Pinus sylvestris **'Hillside' (Creeper)** *g– bright green foliage in summer, yellow-green in winter; dense, prostrate spreading habit; full sun; 4-8"/yr, 2'H/8'W; z3

Pinus sylvestris **'Moseri'** – long twisted medium green needles in summer, golden hued in winter; dense globe form; full sun; 30-36"H/24-30"W; z4

Pinus sylvestris **'Nana Compacta'** *g– short, olive-green needles; compact, wide, rounded shrub form; full sun; 2'H&W; z2

above and above/right: Pinus sylvestris 'Nana Compacta' – This cultivar makes a perfect rock garden specimen with its slow growth and compact form.

below: Pinus sylvestris 'Sentinal'

Pinus sylvestris **'Repens'** – rich blue-green thickened foliage; slow-growing, dense, low mound with irregular outline; full sun; 10"H/2'W; z3

Pinus sylvestris **'Riverside Gem'** *g– bright blue-green needles; compact mound habit; full sun; 2"/yr,3'H/W ; z4

Pinus sylvestris **'Sentinal'** – blue-green needles; dense, narrow columnar habit; full sun; 2-3"/yr, 3'H/18"W; z2

Pinus sylvestris **'Spaan's Slow Column'** – dark green foliage; slow-growing, narrow columnar form; full sun; 1-2"/yr, 2'H/12"H; z4

Pinus sylvestris **'Viridis Compacta'** *g– vivid grass-green twisted foliage; slow-growing open conical form; full sun; 5'H/3'W in 30 yrs; z2 NOTE: more tight columnar form on west coast

Pinus thunbergiana (species) – Japanese Black Pine, aka Kuro-matsu; pairs of thick, rigid, dark grey-green & spiky needles up to 4" long, held in dense bunches; young shoots stand straight up, are long & covered with white silk scales – it looks like it's covered with candles, even more so for the very short time in the early spring when tiny red cones first appear at the tips of the 'candle'; erratically formed & spaced, but generally level branches with tips that turn up; dark purplish grey bark cracking into irregular fissures which become more pronounced with age; form is broadly conical when young; with age, the rugged trunk & irregular branching framework, along with the thick needles & conspicuous white buds, give it character & help distinguish it from other pines; 12"/yr, 10'/H, 100'/UH; z5 Coasts of Japan & south Korea.

Conifers Coming of Age
Pinus thunbergiana

above: Pinus thunbergiana - Close-up of the specimen in the Ellen Gordon Allen Garden at the entrance to the Japanese Pavilion and Stroll Garden. See page 1-4.

***Pinus thunbergiana* 'Thunderhead'** – spectacular early spring showing of clusters of long, silver-white candles against rich, dark green, densely packed needles; tight, low mounding habit; full sun; 3-6"/yr, 4'H/5'W; z5

***Pinus thunbergiana* 'Yatsubusa'** – long, dark green needles; prominent silvery winter buds; striking in spring when covered with clusters of upright candles; mounding, wide spreading habit; full sun; 3"/yr, 3'H/8'W; z5

***Pinus thunbergiana* /Corticosa Group** – a botanical designation - irregular forms with abnormally thick corky bark.

left: Pinus thunbergiana 'Thunderhead' – The spectacular early spring showing of clusters of long, silver-white candles.

below: Pinus thunbergiana 'Yatsubusa' – beginning of the spring candling stage
right: Pinus thunbergiana 'Yatsubusa' – The outline of the low-spreading, slightly mounding form is clearly defined in the winter landscape.

below: Pinus thunbergiana `Yatsubusa' – May 1980   photo by Susan Martin

left: Pinus thunbergiana `Yatsubusa' – Susan Martin rates this in her list of top ten favorites! Late summer of '95, this specimen was destroyed within two weeks after an attack by pine wilt nematode. A strong, healthy plant is the only defense . . . bark beetles, carriers of the pine wilt nematode, go for weakened plants. In this instance, the extended drought — even with irrigating — had weakened this specimen, leaving it susceptible to attack.

Note the praying mantis in the center.

below: Pinus wallichiana `Zebrinia' – open, branching form shown with *Chamaecyparis obtusa* `Spiralis' in foreground. This specimen died in summer '94 after showing signs of stress for several years.   photo by Susan Martin

below: Pinus wallichiana `Zebrinia'
photo courtesy of USNA

Pinus wallichiana (species) – Himalayan Pine, Bhutan Pine, Blue Pine; slender, soft & flexible, up to 8" long needles in clusters of five, the outer surface green, inner surface blue-white, giving overall blue color; whorled, drooping branches, & with age becoming more pendulous, often retaining its branches close to the ground; smooth grey bark becomes darker & fissured with age; broadly conical form; to 130'/UH; z5 Himalayas at altitudes up to 13,000'

Pinus wallichiana `Zebrinia' *g– green-banded with yellow, the needles are long, thin & downward-hanging; graceful open pyramidal form; full sun or part shade; <u>not</u> a dwarf; 12-24"/yr, 12'H/8'W; z6 NOTE: some success to z5 with protection – yellow band gets winter damage if not protected

Platycladus orientalis (species) – fka *Thuja orientalis,* Oriental Arborvitae; lacy bright green branchlets in vertical sprays, foliage similar to *Thuja occidentalis*; ascending branches; symetrical pyramidal form; less hardy than *T. occidentalis*; full sun w/good drainage; to 60'; northern China, Manchuria and Korea NOTE: known for its small, extremely neat, bush-like forms.

Conifers Coming of Age
Platycladus orientalis

above: Platycladus orientalis 'Aurea Nana'
below: Podocarpus macrophyllus

Platycladus orientalis 'Aurea Nana' **•g–** Berckman's Golden Arborvitae; soft, feathery flattened foliage held in upward sprays on erect branches; spring coloring is light yellow-green, turning bright golden-yellow for summer, becoming tinged with brown in fall; round to oval form; full sun; 2'H/1'W; z6

Podocarpus (genus) [po-do-KAR-pus] – Podocarps; 65+ species in warm climates, is second largest genus of conifers (only a few are suitable for gardens); thick, often hard, pointed foliage arranged spirally on the shoots; generally dioecious; colorful fruits have a single hard seed embedded in the end of a fleshy colored stalk; mostly evergreen shrubs & trees; z7; Americas from Mexico southwards, central & sourthern Africa, Asia from the Himalayas to Japan & Austrialia

Podocarpus macrophyllus (species) [mak-ro-FIL-us–large-leaved] – Yew Podocarpus; long, thick, leathery, tapered foliage is rich grass-green above, with 2 broad glaucous stomatal bands beneath; dense foliage; irregular upright form; full sun; 8'H/3'W, 50'/UH; z7 eastern China & Japan

Pseudolarix amabilis (species) [soo-do-LAR-iks–false larch–a-MUH-bi-lis–lovely] **•g–** Golden Larch, fka *P.kaemferi* and *Larix amabilis*; long & soft, lush light green needles appear in spring, color deepens in summer, turning a clear yellow in early fall, then to rusty-brown before falling; single leaves are up to 2' long, appearing in whorls on upcruved, short shoots, male cone flowers are in bunches on short spurs, the females on separate branches of the same tree; multitudes of small green cones, –look a bit like small rosettes – ripen in autumn & break up while still on the tree; broad conical form; full sun; 10'H in 10 yrs, 50'/UH; z6 southern China

Pseudotsuga menziesii (species), [SOO-do-tsoo-ga–false evergreen–men-ZEES-I–named after Archibald Menzies] – Douglas Fir; soft, medium green leaves 3/4 to 1-1/4" long, with two white bands on the underside; distinct cones have three-pronged protruded bracts; holds cones from previous year – pyramidal form; 350-300'; z5; British Columbia to California, Montana, Colorado and New Mexico

> Note: See *"The Trees of North America"* by Alan Mitchell for an interesting history of this species..

above, below and right: Pseudotsuga menziesii var. glauca – early May –
This species at the Arboretum is a a naturally occurring variety with
blue-green needles.

Pseudotsuga menziesii 'Densa' *g— too good to pass up! I must quote this description given by Charles Harrison in *"Ornamental Conifers"*, "....an irregular, dumpy little heap of cheerful, dark-green foliage bearing little resemblance to its towering forest parent, apart from foliage detail." (The foliage is better described as medium green, otherwise, what a wonderful description!); full sun; 2"/yr; z5

above: *Pseudotsuga menziesii* 'Densa'

Sciadopitys verticillata (species) [si-a-DOP-I-tis—umbrella—ver-ti-si-LAW-tuh—whorled] — Japanese Umbrella Pine; long, narrow, thick, stiff shiny dark green needles in whorls of 10-30 radiate outwards from stem like ribs of an umbrella; reddish brown bark; looks like a tropical pine tree; pyramidal form; sun to light shade; 6-12"/yr, 4'H/2'W, 60'/UH in 50+ yrs; z4; Japan

Sequoiadendron giganteum (species) [se-KWOY-a-den-dron—named for a Cherokee Indian, Sequoyah—dendron = a tree] — minute, lance-like leaves completely surround the branchlets; tiny green conelets take 2 yrs to mature, then may remain on tree up to 20 yrs; bark can be 2' thick; can live three to four thousand years; narrowly conical form; full sun; 325-365'/UH with up to 30' diameter trunk; roots of a single tree can cover 4 acres; z7; Sierra Nevada Mountains of California   NOTE: The trunk of the General Grant tree is estimated to weigh six thousand tons, with enough board footage to construct fifty six-room homes. This is the species where you see pictures of tourists driving through in their autos.

above: *Sciadopitys verticillata*
photo by Susan Martin

Sequoiadendron giganteum 'Hazel Smith' *g— striking blue foliage; full-sized pyramidal form; full sun; 18-30"/yr, 18'H/10'W; z6

Taxodium distichum (species) [taks-O-dee-um DIS-ti-kum] — Bald Cypress or Swamp Cypress; deciduous foliage arranged in two flat flanks, similar to *Taxus*, has a delicate, feathery appearance; fresh yellow-green needles in spring, darkening for summer, then turning russet in fall; roots develop "cypress knees" when grown near water, or with plenty of moisture; full sun, tolerates part shade; fast-growing, <u>not</u> a dwarf; narrow when young, pyramidal as it matures with long level branches; 2-4'/yr, 16'H/8'W, 60'/UH; z5 south-eastern USA, New Jersey to Texas

below:
Sequoiadendron giganteum 'Hazel Smith' — Named in honor of Hazel Smith; wife of Don Smith of Watnong Nurseries, and donors of the Watnong Collection.

below: *Taxodium distichum* 'Pendens', its foliage still carpeting the ground beneath it; the rounded form behind/left is *Picea abies* 'Maxwellii'; and front/right, large mounding form with gracefully pendulous branchlets — *Tsuga canadensis* 'Pendula'

below: *Sequoiadendron giganteum* 'Hazel Smith'   photo by Susan Martin

Conifers Coming of Age
Taxodium distichum

above: knees' of *Taxodium distichum* 'Pendens' - 1st of January
photo by Susan Martin

above: *Taxodium distichum* 'Pendens' –
'knees' and spring foliage - 1st of May

above: *Taxus x media* 'Flushing'

below: *Taxus x media*
photo courtesy of USNA

Taxodium distichum 'Pendens' *g– Weeping Bald Cypress; similar in every way to the species except for the long, graceful, pendulous branches; z5['62]

Taxus (genus) [TAX-us] – Yew; rich dark green needles about 1" long; plants are *dioecious* (having male & female flowers on separate plants); female plants bear single seeds, carried in fleshy red cups (the *aril*, commonly referred to as 'berries'), & appear like scarlet berries in the fall; tolerate alkaline & acid soils; withstands drought conditions, doesn't tolerate wet feet; full sun to light shade

Taxus baccata (species) – English Yew; lustrous dark green leaves, show contrast against light green of young shoots; slow-growing, densely-branched tree to 40+ feet; Europe, northern Africa & western Asia

Taxus baccata 'Fastigiata' – Irish Yew; dark, green-black leaves; sharply ascending branches; columnar when young, older plants become more branched and wider at the top; full sun, tolerates partial shade; 6"/yr, 6-10'H/12"W; z5

Taxus baccata 'Procumbens' – medium green foliage; branches spread at right angles to the stem; less than 2"/yr, 3'H/4'W; full sun; z6

Taxus baccata 'Standishii' – Golden English Yew; small green needles with bright yellow margin; red berries in winter; slow-growing upright dense columnar form; sun to part shade; 4-5'H/1'W; z6

Taxus cuspidata (species) – Japanese Yew; dull, dark green leaves on short, yellowish stalks; wide-spreading or ascending branches to 50'; Japan, Korea & Manchuria

Taxus cuspidata 'Luteobaccata' – Japanese Yew; dark green needles; irregular shrubby habit; yellow berries; sun or shade; 6"/yr; z5

Taxus x media (species) – Anglo-Japanese Yew; hybrid between T. cuspidata and T. baccatta; hardier and stronger growing than parent plants

Taxus x media 'Flushing' – large, shiny dark green needles; stately upright columnar form; bright red berries; rich, red-brown bark; shade or full sun; 4'H/18"W; z4

Taxus x media 'Hicksii' – large, glossy deep green needles; fast-growing erect columnar form; bright red berries; shade or full sun; 12'H/6'W at maturity; z4

Thuja (genus) [THOO-ya] – Arborvitae; only five-six species; flat, fan-shaped clusters of branchlets completely covered with overlapping pairs of scale-like leaves (called "adult" types), some dwarf varieties have persistent spine-like leaves (called "juvenile" types) that stand out from the branchlets like tiny flat spines or needles, some cultivars have foliage that changes from juvenile to adult (called "transitional" types), branchlets held in flat, upright sprays; crushed foliage has a characteristic scent; male & female cones on same tree; mostly tall pyramidal form; North America & northeast Asia.

Thuja occidentalis (species) — American Arborvitae; bright green color changing to dull brownish-green or brownish-yellow in winter; pyramidal form; fast-growing to 70'; North America

***Thuja occidentalis* 'Emerald Green'** — aka *T.o.* 'Smaragd'; bright, glossy emerald green foliage, holding color in winter; dense pyramidal form; full sun; 6'H/3'W; z3

***Thuja occidentalis* 'Filiformis'** — Threadleaf Arborvitae; long trailing branchlets with rich green foliage pressed tight against stem creating a cord-like effect; distinctive orange-brown arching branches; amber winter foliage in colder climates; low sprawling rounded form; full sun; 30"H&W, 3'H/4'W in 30 yrs; z4

***Thuja occidentalis* 'Globosa Rheindiana'** *g— medium green foliage in tufts, somewhat congested; rounded globe form; full sun; 2"/yr, 2'H/3'W; z4

***Thuja occidentalis* 'Hetz Midget'** — dense, diminutive, dark green foliage in crowded sprays; turns brown in winter; extremely slow-growing compact globe form; full sun; 1-3"/yr, 1'H&W, 18"H/4½'W in 30 yrs; z3

right and below: Thuja occidentalis 'Hetz Midget' — flowing branch structure is revealed on this mature specimen.

below: Thuja occidentalis 'Filiformis' - This winter coloring could be described as 'ratty' or 'interesting', depending on the eyes of the beholder. It can be a nice choice for contrasting color and form in the winter landscape. I have a young specimen of this plant, and by the end of the first winter, I was sure it was dead. I was quite relieved when it "greened up" as summer drew near. Then after the harsh winter that followed, it looked like it really had succumbed – I actually counted it among my losses! Suffice to say, it becomes more graceful and interesting with age!

Conifers Coming of Age
Thuja occidentalis

above: Thuja occidentalis 'Rheingold' – left: late April; right: mid-March. This cultivar is an asset in the landscape with its light, soft-looking foliage and gently mounding form – Its seasonal color changes are a bonus, making it even more desirable. It is a popular cultivar, and fairly easy to find.

above: Thuja occidentalis 'Rheingold' – early June   photo courtesy of USNA

***Thuja occidentalis* 'Holmstudji'** — rich green flattened foliage grows in tightly packed vertical sprays, turns slightly bronze in winter; compact, narrowly pyramidal form; full sun; 4'H/2'W; z4

***Thuja occidentalis* 'Rheingold'** *g— soft, feathery yellow-orange tipped juvenile foliage, pale green w/yellow overtones–spring, bright green w/golden overtones–summer, rich coppery bronze–winter; broad mounding habit; full sun for best color contrasts; 3-6"/yr; 3'H/4'W; 5'W/7'H in 30 yrs; z3

***Thuja occidentalis* 'Sunkist'** — dense, flattened sprays of orange-yellow foliage in winter, lemon-yellow in spring; dwarf pyramidal form; full sun; 3-6"/yr, 4'H/2-3'W; z3

***Thuja occidentalis* 'Tiny Tim'** — dense mid-green foliage; finely branched; very small globose form; on of the dwarfest *T.o.*; full sun; 16"H/12"W; z4

***Thuja occidentalis* 'Wareana Lutescens'** *g— cream to pale yellow flattened sprays of foliage with a sheen in summer, giving a silvery white overlay look in winter; wide pyramidal form; full sun; 2-3"/yr, 7'H/4'W in 35 yrs; z4

***Thuja occidentalis* 'Woodwardii'** *g— lacy flat fans of dark green foliage, slightly bronze in winter; retains globe form without trimming; full sun; 2"/yr, 3'H&W, 7'H/5'W in 35 yrs; z4

left and below: Thuja occidentalis 'Wareana Lutescens' – winter foliage
photos by Susan Martin

Thuja orientalis – see *Platycladus orientalis*

Thujopsis dolabrata (species) – Hiba, Oriental Arborvitae; heavy, flat sprays of foliage, shiny bright green above, silvery white beneath; dark, reddish brown bark peels in grey strips; broad shrub form with conical crown; 100'/UH, only 65'/UH in cultivation; full sun w/good drainage; z5 Japan

Thujopsis dolabrata 'Nana' – bright green fine-textured overlapping scale-like foliage, marked with silver on reverse side thick; remains bright-green in winter; upward pointed sprays, spreading bun-shaped mound; full sun/lt shade; 2'H/4'W; z6

Thujopsis dolabrata var. hondai – glossy green scale-like foliage in fans, similar in appearance to *Thuja occidentalis*, but almost double the size; prominent glaucous markings on back of branchlet; course in texture; wide pyramidal form; full sun; 6-10"/yr, 100'/UH; z5 northern Japan

below and right: Thujopsis dolabrata 'Nana'

Tsuga (genus) [TSOO-ga] – Hemlock; about ten species; lustrous, flat, small dark green needles; elegant, drooping, irregular-length branches; hold small woody cones after seed drop; wide pyramidal form (elegant & graceful are the best words to describe this genus!); good in acidic soil, shade tolerant, with many cultivars requiring partial shade; North America & Asia

photo by Susan Martin

Tsuga canadensis (species) – Canada Hemlock; ½" long, shining dark green needles irregularly arranged but mainly appearing in two opposite ranks; usually multiple trunks; irregular pyramidal form; 100'/UH; z4 eastern North America

Tsuga canadensis 'Albospica' – new shoots are white contrasting against mature dark green needles; arching branches & loose upright growth, wide pyramidal form; light shade; 6'H/2'W; z4

Tsuga canadensis –Winter burn can be a problem with variegated cultivars.

Tsuga canadensis 'Beaujean' – aka 'Saratoga Broom'; light green foliage; low-spreading, thick fan-like branches; branches spread upward and outward, leaving a cone-shaped depression in the top center of the shrub; sun to partial shade; 4'H/2'W; z4

below: Tsuga canadensis 'Beaujean' in front, and in back, looking somewhat like a huge Hershey® Kiss – Tsuga canadensis 'Brandley'

Tsuga canadensis 'Bennett' *g– dark green foliage; arched, graceful, ascending branches with pendulous tips; mounding form; partial shade; 3-6"/yr, 30-36"H&W; z4

Tsuga canadensis 'Boulevard' – somewhat longer and more densely set, very dark green foliage; irregular

Conifers Coming of Age
Tsuga canadensis

*above: Tsuga canadensis 'Brandley' –
This delicate green spring foliage
against the deep, shiny green mature
foliage can give the appearance that it
is decorated, especially so when
there's an abundance of cones.*

There are three specimens of this cultivar in the Gotelli Collection, each one a totally different size and form, yet they're all about the same age. The one pictured above is on the high side of a steep, dry embankment, is about 6'W/4'H with open, and has comparatively sparse, somewhat irregular and open branching. The one pictured on the previous page might have had its top damaged at some time, restricting the top growth. Otherwise, it has thick, dense, almost lush, uniform growth. The one pictured on page 2-8 definitely has lush, uniform growth, and is approaching 20'H/12'W.

It would be hard to believe these three specimens are the same cultivar. This variation can be attributed to the differences in cultural conditions of each of the specimens. Commonly referred to as 'micro-climates,' many gardens have this wide range of cultural conditions, and could expect similar results.

length branches; compact pyramidal form; partial shade; 4-5"/yr, 5'H/4'W, 18'H/12'W in 30 yrs; z4

***Tsuga canadensis* 'Brandley'** *g– large, dark green needles; slow-growing, dense, compact globose to conical habit; partial shade; 3'H/2'W; z4

***Tsuga canadensis* 'Cappy's Choice'** – fine-textured, light green foliage, slight golden hue; low-growing pendulous form; partial shade; 18"H&W; z4

***Tsuga canadensis* 'Cole's Prostrate'** – dark green foliage; slightly mounding, spreading prostrate form; as it matures, gray branches become exposed in the center giving it an 'ancient' look; extremely slow-growing, Gotelli described it as a "...true dwarf"; especially effective in the rock garden where the foliage can gracefully cascade over a rock; must have partial shade; 2-3"/yr, 10-15"H/2-3'W, 12-18"H/5-6'W in 35 yrs; z4

***Tsuga canadensis* 'Curly'** – dark green needles turning downward on the ends; stiff, brittle branches; irregular, somewhat contorted, upright form; partial

*above, right, below:
Tsuga canadensis
'Cole's Prostrate'*

above: Tsuga canadensis 'Curly' – new lime green spring growth cover branchlet tips in tiny, tight tufts, looking like miniature florets — especially outstanding and noticeable against the contrasting mature dark green foliage.

above: Tsuga canadensis 'Great Lakes' in back; Tsuga canadensis 'Greenspray' in front

***Tsuga canadensis* 'Cushion' *g–** dense, short, stiff, very fine textured needles; neat bun form; partial shade; 1-3"/yr; 3'H&W in 30 yrs; z4

***Tsuga canadensis* 'Great Lakes' –** dark green foliage; ascending branches and short branchlets; loose, upright conical habit; multi-stemmed; partial shade; 2-5"/yr, 10'H/6'W in 35 yrs; z4

***Tsuga canadensis* 'Greenspray' –** medium green foliage; graceful fan-like boughs; wide fountain form; partial shade; 3-6"/yr; z3

***Tsuga canadensis* 'Guldemond's Dwarf' –** medium green short needles, densely packed on short; compact irregular pyramidal form; partial shade; 2"/yr; z3

***Tsuga canadensis* 'Henry Hohman' –** dense, dark green foliage; short, stiff branches; upright conical habit with short, stiff lateral branches giving it a rugged twiggy outline; partial shade; 2-4"/yr; z4

***Tsuga canadensis* 'Hussii' –** short, twiggy branchlets; irregular upright outline; partial shade; 2-4"/yr, 2'H/1'W; z4

***Tsuga canadensis* 'Jacqueline Verkade' –** medium green, soft, tiny foliage on tiny stems; dwarf conical form; partial shade; 1-3"/yr, 18"H/14"W; z4

***Tsuga canadensis* 'Jervis' –** congested, dark green foliage; crowded, irregular branchlets; slow-growing, irregular upright habit; partial shade; 1-3"/yr, 1'H/6"W; z4

***Tsuga canadensis* 'Kelsey's Weeping' –** long graceful pendulous branches; asymmetrical form; partial shade; 4-6"/yr, 4'H/3'W; z4

***Tsuga canadensis* 'Minima' –** short spreading branchlets, weeping branch tips; arching branches, partial shade; 4-6"/yr, 2'H/3'W, 7'H/6'H in 30 yrs; z4

***Tsuga canadensis* 'Minuta' –** rich dark green congested foliage; extremely dwarf irregular shape; breeds true from seed; partial shade; 1/4"/yr, only 2' at 50 years; z4

***Tsuga canadensis* 'Nana' –** fine textured needles; dense branching; nest-shaped low mound form; partial shade; 2"/yr; z4

Conifers Coming of Age
Tsuga canadensis

above: The wide pyramidal form on the left is *Tsuga canadensis* /Jenkins seedling/, the middle specimen, much larger than you'd expect with a name like *Tsuga canadensis* 'Minima', and the rounded form on the right is *Tsuga canadensis* 'Cushion', which was introduced through nursery trade by USNA. Gotelli's was one of the few in existence.

left: Tsuga canadensis 'Minima' – mid-March

above: Tsuga canadensis 'Muttontown'
below:
    Tsuga canadensis 'Verkade's Recurved'

Tsuga canadensis '**Pendula**' – Weeping Hemlock; medium green foliage; broad, arching, overlapping pendulous branches; stake to desired height; partial shade, can tolerate full sun; 3'H/5'W; z4

Tsuga canadensis '**Sargentii**' – Sargent's Weeping Hemlock; medium green foliage; mounds of overlapping, pendulous branches; broad, spreading, irregular habit; partial shade to full sun; 6-12"/yr; z3

Tsuga canadensis '**Stranger**' *g– rich green heavy textured foliage; irregular upright form, as broad as high; partial shade; 3'H/W; z4

Tsuga canadensis '**Stockman's Dwarf**' – short, medium green, densely spaced needles; closely layered branches; upright conical form; partial shade; 3'H/2'W; z4

Tsuga canadensis '**Verkade's Recurved**' – medium green twisting needles; slow-growing open habit, stiff brittle upright branches; partial shade; 24-30"H/12-18"W; z4

Tsuga canadensis '**Vermeulen's Pyramid**' – dense foliage; rapid growing, tall slender pyramid; partial shade; 1"/yr; z3 NOTE: new cultivar

Tsuga canadensis '**Von Helms**' – rich medium green foliage; dense, pyramidal form; partial shade; 4"/yr, 9'H/5' W in 30 yrs; z3

Tsuga canadensis '**Watnong Star**' – almost white new growth at tips has star-like appearance; soft globe form; partial shade; z4

Tsuga diversifolia (species) — Northern Japanese Hemlock; dark green foliage, new growth twists, showing silvery reverse; semi-dwarf upright, bushy, irregular form; sun or light shade; 4'H/2'W; z5

above: *Tsuga diversifolia* – The stomatic bands are so bright and conspicuous that the popular name in Japan is "The Rice Tree"

For growth comparisons, check your library for Charles R. Harrison's book, *Ornamental Conifers*, published by Hafner Press in 1975. Many of Harrison's photos were taken at the USNA in the early 70's, when the Gotelli Collection had been in place about ten years. You'll see many of the same specimens shown in this book as they looked 20-25 years ago.

Special acknowledgment is given to the Brooklyn Botanic Garden for permission to use the handbook *Dwarf Conifers*, published by the Garden in 1965 and 1984, as a source for most of the species descriptions given in this chapter. For information on becoming a Subscribing Member, which entitles you to four handbooks in the new *21st Century Gardening Series* and a subscription to *Plants & Gardens News*, write Brooklyn Botanic Garden, 1000 Washington Ave., Brooklyn, NY 11225, or call (718) 622-4433 ext. 260.

Special thanks and gratitude to Susan F. Martin for all her encouragement, contributions, help & time spent going over the pieces & parts & building of this chapter! If the nomenclature is accurate, we can all thank Susan: If it isn't, it probably slipped through without being confirmed by Susan. She has been incredibly patient and extremely helpful! I cannot thank her enough.

Keys used throughout this chapter:

Botanical name — common name (listed under each species); foliage color, shape and outstanding characteristics; overall form and growth characteristics; unusual or unique characteristics or requirements; sun/shade requirements; growth rates when available — average growth rate per year ('/yr'), expected height & width ('H/W') in ten years, ultimate height ('/UH'); minimum cold hardiness zone ('z'). Country of origin (species only).

1-3'/yr = average growth rate per year is between one to three inches

1'H/3'W = expected size in ten years – one foot high by three feet wide

13'/UH = ulitimate height is thirteen feet

z = minimum cold hardiness zone according to the USDA hardiness map

Conifers Coming of Age

above: Tsuga canadensis 'Pendula' – This spot is on the edge of the clearing between beds 1 and 2, blending into the decidous woods behind. Many of Gotelli's cultivars and azaleas are planted amongst these woods where they thrive in the partial shade.

Take It With You

Take this book along with you as a handy reference when you're shopping. Then, when you're considering a specific cultivar, referring to this chapter can help. If the particular cultivar you're seeking hasn't been included, you can refer to its species description. From there, you'll have a general idea of the necessary growing conditions, and how well it should fare in your own garden.

Care & Maintenance 6
Including
Integrated Pest Management

Conifers are among the toughest, most cold-hardy evergreens, and are considered the backbone and `work-horses' of every garden. With many dwarf forms becoming more widely available, even the smallest garden can boast a few choice specimens. These plants have a tremendous variety in growth habit, texture, color and seasonal changes. Their beauty is long lasting, whether they are used as specimen plants, foundation plants, in a mixed shrub border, as an evergreen hedge, and/or as accents in perennial and rock gardens. Dwarf conifers are an interesting addition to home landscapes for many reasons:

- slow growth rates
- low maintenance
- unique forms/sizes/shapes
- colors — from bluest blue to bright yellow
- textures of foliage/bark
- seasonal/year-round interest
    - √ color changes in foliage/bark
    - √ outline/silhouette — especially when highlighted with snow

Cultural Considerations

Most of the conifers in the Gotelli collection are adaptable to a wide range of conditions. Susan Martin, the curator for the Gotelli collection, describes these conifers as "very durable". After each period of extreme weather she gets to find out just how 'hardy' and 'durable' the various specimens are by checking out the extent of damages. The wide variety of seasonal changes in the Washington, D.C. area has been ideal for many cultivars, while some have merely survived — and some have succumbed. Susan said that she feels the cultivars that are still thriving from the original 1962 plantings are truly 'survivors'!

Hardiness Zone

Zone tolerance and hardiness should be one of the very first considerations when choosing a plant. To say a plant 'tolerates' a particular zone does not necessarily mean that it **thrives** in that zone. A few of the more conscientious nursery people are providing zone information for their plants including both the 'ideal' and the 'tolerable' zone information. 'Tolerable' may mean you have a much smaller, slower growing, but otherwise healthy specimen — which can be ideal for a rock garden, container gardening or when space is limited.

By taking advantage of existing 'micro-climates', together with proper winter protection, it is possible to enjoy some of the plants that would not survive without this extra effort.

Weather Extremes

The beauty of an ice storm
Photos by Scott Aker

Winters in Washington, D.C. vary from wet and cool to extreme cold accompanied by desiccating icy winds. It does not get the snow cover needed to insulate and protect plants from extreme temperature fluctuations. The native habitats of many conifers usually provide snow protection. Without snow protection conifers can be damaged by freezing, dehydrating winds. During very cold winters, damage results in burned foliage on Deodar cedar (*Cedrus deodara*) and Japanese cedar (*Cryptomeria*). This damage is not usually permanent, but may cause dieback of branch tips and terminal branches.

Damage occurs from winter wind when the ground is frozen and a plant's roots cannot replenish lost moisture. The combination of sun and wind during winter when the ground is still frozen, particularly if its over a prolonged period of time, can be especially harmful.

Summers in Washington, D.C. are hot and humid, with some years of near drought conditions. Firs (*Abies*) and spruce (*Picea*) suffer in the heat, while the junipers (*Juniperus*) flourish. Plant hardiness with regard to conifers in Washington, D.C. usually equates with how <u>heat</u> tolerant the plants are rather than how cold hardy they are.

Soil Conditions

Soil conditions are important. Most conifers prefer a moist, aerated, well-drained soil with a neutral to slightly acid Ph. The yews (*Taxus*) and junipers excel in soils closer to neutral, while false cypress (*Chamaecyparis*), pines (*Pinus*), spruce and firs require soils in the more acid range. Heavy clay soils need to be amended.

Consider planting your conifers on a slight mound to help improve drainage. Mounds can add variety and interest, aid air flow and water drainage. Also, mound planting allows <u>you</u> to control the content of the soil in that mound. The ideal soil would be sandy loam, slightly on the acid side. Well-decomposed organic amendments such as leaf humus not only helps improve drainage, it also provides natural nutrients.

Choosing the Best Location

Many cultivars only display their color when planted in direct sun, while others require the benefit of afternoon shading so as not to 'sunburn'. Blue cultivars often benefit from light shade. Most yellow cultivars prefer full sun. Most of the hemlocks (*Tsuga)* need protection from direct afternoon sun.

Consider your 'winter scene' when choosing a planting site. Some cultivars turn yellow only in winter, while other cultivars take on a plum coloration. Take full advantage of these qualities to enhance your winter landscape.

Get acquainted with the description and requirements of your particular cultivar. Learning about the species of the cultivar gives you an idea of the natural growing conditions, which in turn gives you an idea of your cultivar's requirements. Knowing what to expect saves you from disappointment later.

Ice Storms

Ice storms can be breathtakingly beautiful and close to impossible to describe. A person must see to believe, and even then there is such an ethereal fairy-land quality to it, that even seeing it doesn't make it seem real.

But the damage caused by an ice storm is real enough — it can be devastating! Huge limbs can snap under the weight, and otherwise sturdy trees can split down the middle.

Winter Protection

Although stratigically impractical at the Arboretum, a few winter protection methods can make a difference in the extent of winter damage.

- Mulching can protect roots from alternating freezing/thawing that often occurs in northern climates where there isn't a constant protective snow cover.

- Columnar specimens especially can benefit when the branches are tied together to help prevent splitting.

- Wrapping with burlap can help prevent splitting of multi-stemmed specimens. Burlap can also be used to help protect sensitive cultivars from winter winds and winter sunburn.

Planting and Transplanting

Buy plants with a sturdy root system to insure greater success. It is worth checking out – especially container grown plants. Is it root bound? Are the roots dead or dying from too much or too little water? Look for the full white tips of new growth as an indication of healthy roots.

Conifers are shallow rooted plants that transplant best with an adequate root ball. Early spring and fall are ideal times for planting with the cooler temperatures and (generally) more rainfall. Fall planting is preferred in D.C. because the heat and humidity of other seasons can stress the plants, and plants under stress are easy targets for disease and insect infestation. In colder climates, plant early enough in the fall to allow adequate time for root development before the hard freezes.

Planting in the Soil

The hole should be prepared in advance of planting. It should be a wide, shallow hole, with the depth just deep enough to hold the root ball. The width should be half again as wide as the root ball. It is no longer recommended that the hole be deeper than the root ball. The bottom of the hole should just be loosened and disturbed, but not dug deeply.

After you have dug the hole, fill the hole with water, then wait about a half hour. This is to insure that there is plenty of moisture surrounding the new planting, but also, in that amount of time, the water should be absorbed. If it is not, you should take steps to improve the drainage. Adding organic matter is not recommended unless the soil is compact or has a high clay content (mound plantings may be the exception).

Planting from Containers

Tap around the side of the container with your hand or shovel handle. This loosens the roots from the side of the pot. Next, place your hand on top of the pot, spreading your fingers so that you can support both the stem and the top of the soil. Turn the pot upside-down and gently remove the container with your free hand.

If there are roots protruding from the drain holes that won't slide out with the plant, cut them off with your pruners so the plant slides free. If the plant is pot-bound, the roots will be in a dense mat. Gently cut through some of the larger roots with your pruners, then loosen the ball a little by working the rest of the roots free. Now it is ready to plant.

Transplanting Mature Specimen

When a mature plant outgrows its site, moving it can often mean losing it. By taking a few simple steps (literally) the fall and spring previous to when you move it, the plant can be moved with a minimum of trauma.

The object is to sever the roots ahead of time, allowing the plant to develop new roots close to the root ball. A sharp spade will usually suffice –

The year before the planned move (this takes planning), sever the roots at the 12:00 o'clock position, the 3:00, 6:00, and 9:00 o'clock positions. You want to sever them inside the circle you will eventually be digging when you lift the root ball. In the fall (assuming you started in the spring), sever the roots at the 1:30, 4:30, 7:30 and 10:30 positions.

The following spring (this is a full year from the original root pruning), allow plenty of room for the circle of new roots as you dig the rootball. The newly developed roots help the plant re-establish itself faster, and with less stress.

Planting from Balled and Burlapped (B&B)

B&B plants require gentle handling to insure that the root ball is not disturbed or broken apart.

If the plant is wrapped in plastic "burlap" or treated burlap (which may be green in color), then the burlap should be carefully removed from the root ball before you plant. These burlaps will not decompose and could girdle the plant, eventually killing it. Also, remove all artificial twine before planting for the same reason. These **must** be discarded before planting. If it is **natural** burlap laced with **natural** string or rope or pinned with nails, set the entire plant in the prepared hole. Cut the burlap away from the trunk of the plant and roll it back to expose the top of the soil.

Step back and check that your hole is the right depth. The top of the root ball should be about 1″ higher than the existing soil level. Be sure to cut away the burlap about half way down the sides of the plant and discard it, otherwise it will wick away moisture. You can leave the rest of the burlap **if it is natural**.

Transplanting Freshly Dug Plants

The object is to minimize the trauma to the plant. Take as much of the root ball and as much surrounding soil as possible, trying not to disturb the roots. Wrapping the rootball with burlap helps keep the rootball in tact. Even when moving just a short distance, wrapping the rootball can make an enormous difference in the plant's recovery.

The Planting

When you first place the plant in the hole, the root ball should be about one inch above the existing soil level. Back fill some soil around the base of the plant, packing firmly around the root ball to eliminate air pockets. Water the plant. When the water has soaked in, continue to back fill with soil until the soil level is level with the root ball's outer edge. Water the plant again. If the soil level drops, add enough to bring it level with the root ball.

When the planting is done, place mulch 3" deep around the plant, taking care not to mulch too close to the trunk. Water the plants thoroughly immediately after planting and continue to do so during any periods of drought until the plants are well established. This may take two to three years — be especially attentive the first year. It is best to water thoroughly once a week, rather than daily sprinkling. As a general rule, until the conifers are well established they need the equivalent of an inch of rainfall each week.

Transplanting Seedlings & Container Plants

Seedlings

After the second set of true leaves are developed is the best time to transplant seedlings. Avoid waiting too long or the seedlings become overcrowded. They can be transplanted into a flat, individual cell packs or pots.

Seedlings going into a flat - Using a sterile media, fill the flat to the top, then gently pack the media into the flat. It should be firm, but not tightly compacted. Next, using a dibble or a pencil, gently lift the seedling from the germination flat, make a hole in the transplanting flat (deep enough to accommodate the seedling's root system), gently set the seedling in the new hole at the same depth it was in the germination tray. Press the soil firmly around the seedling's root system to avoid air pockets. Fill the flat, spacing the seedlings 2-3" apart and water thoroughly. Keep the flat shaded the first few days. Do not allow it to dry out.

Seedlings going into a cell pack or pot - This is actually the preferred method as it makes handling of the seedlings at the next planting stage a lot easier. The method of transplanting is the same as above.

Container to Container

The method is the same, regardless of the size of the container; from 3" pot, to patio tub.

When transplanting from cell packs, gently squeeze the edges of the cell to loosen the soil from the edge of the pot. Then push up on the bottom of the cell so that it pushes the soil ball and plant free of the pack, at the same time, holding the pack so your free hand can cradle the plant and soil once it is free.

Use the same method for pot to pot transplanting except that instead of pushing up on the bottom of the pot which is more rigid than a cell-pack, you place a hand across the top of the pot, straddling the plant, turn the pot and plant on it's side, then gently tap the upper rim of the pot on a table or the floor until the plant slides free. Now is the time to evaluate the plant you are holding in your hand (or is it a larger specimens lying on the floor?!)

Roots – What is their condition?

Disturb the roots a little when transplanting smaller plants that are not pot-bound, gently breaking apart the bottom of the soil ball. The plant establishes itself more quickly.

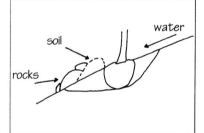

Planting on a hill – extra soil should be placed on the lowest side of the hole, reinforcing with carefully placed rocks. The object is to catch the rain without loosing the soil in the process.

When transplanting larger or pot-bound specimens, it is best to evaluate the plant for a few moments to decide how much to disturb the root system before transplanting.

Most plants have a fibrous root system which becomes pot-bound if left in the same pot too long. Pot-bound plants can eventually girdle or strangle themselves if the encircling roots are not broken apart. For moderately pot-bound plants you can break apart the root ball using your hands or a pair of pruning shears to loosen and free the roots. For large pot-bound plants, a slice through the root ball with a spade or shovel to "butterfly" the ball will usually prevent girdling.

Select a pot or container one size larger than the one the plant came out of. Too small a pot will cause the plant to become root-bound again and stunt plant growth. Too large a pot cause the plant to decline also. the pot is too large, the extra soil tends to stay wet too long, and the roots actually decline instead of regenerate.

The soil level needs to be ½-1" below the rim of the pot, allowing room for watering. To start, firm a small amount of the planting media in the bottom of the pot. Hold the plant still in the container with one hand to keep it upright while scooping media around the plant with your free hand. Remember to firm the media to prevent air pockets around the roots.

... and last but not least: Always water the plant thoroughly when you are finished.

Maintenance

One of the many benefits of growing dwarf conifers is that they only require minimal maintenance. They need mulch, water, very little (if any) fertilizing, and very little (if any) pruning. In other words – very little maintenance!

Mulch

You get a healthier plant and less work when you use mulch. Mulching helps to retain moisture, keep the soil temperature more constant, and control weeds. It should be about three inches deep, keeping it away from the base of the plant. The best mulches to use with conifers would be pine bark mulch, shredded hardwood bark, pine needles or stones.

Mice damage to *Juniperus procumbens* 'Nana'   Photo courtesy of USNA

Choices

Your initial choice of plants makes a difference in your overall maintenance requirements.

By choosing to grow "resistant" plants, you improve your chances of having healthy plants. Resistance does not mean that plants are immune to pest or disease problems, but that they are able to withstand attacks from pests and diseases without any long-term damage.

An example is the rodent damage to the *Juniperus procumbens* 'Nana' plants at the Arboretum. *Juniperus conferta* 'Blue Lagoon', a juniper which has shown immunity to rodent damage, has recently been introduced as an alternative.

Given a choice of junipers, choosing the rodent resistant cultivar can make a difference between a healthy plant needing very little maintenance, and one that is continuously stressed, needing constant maintenance.

Watering

The first three years after planting, when the roots are getting established, regular wating is important. During the first year after planting, consistant ground moisture is crucial. A deep watering once a week - from rain or irrigation - is usually what is needed. The first few months after planting, more frequent watering may be necessary. Surrounding influences, such as sidewalks, driveways, elevated beds, drainage ditches and deciduous trees wick away ground mosisture — monitor plants near these 'features', as they are likely to require much more watering.

At the Arboretum, all new plantings are monitored for watering needs, particularly their first year, and often into their third year. If it goes more than one week without measurable rainfall, young plantings are watered, plus those specimens near the deciduous trees. As a general rule, any time a dry period goes into the third week, everything gets water. By then, even the well-established, mature specimens will be stressed if they are not watered. When a drought persists, frequent monitoring can help prevent stress to the plants.

As a general guide, water the equivelent of one inch of rain every week, although the specific needs of individual specimens vary.

Fertilizing

Established dwarf conifers that are growing well seldom, if ever, need to be fertilized. Keep size and growth rate in mind when you fertilize. Heavy fertilizing can result in abnormally increased growth. If you do fertilize, choose balanced fertilizers that aren't too high in nitrogen. Basic garden fertilizers such as 5-10-5 to 10-10-10 are good choices and should be applied (according to directions) in March, prior to the spring flush of growth. Generally, the dwarf conifers at the Arboretum get fertilized the first three years after planting. After that, they are usually well enough established that fertilizing is not needed.

Pruning

Broken or dead branches need to be pruned out immediately regardless of the time of year. Selective pruning can enhance the natural structure of many cultivars. Following are a few rules to keep in mind if you are doing more drastic pruning:

√ Most conifers grow solely from the branch tip. (Broad-leaved plants have buds along the entire branches that will usually grow when stimulated by pruning.) Yews (*Taxus*), arborvitae (*Thuja occidentalis*) and some pines will send out new interior growth as a result of

Pruning Dead Branches

Dead branches need to be pruned out as soon as possible, regardless of the time of year.

Photos by Susan Martin

pruning. Most conifers, however, do not break buds on older wood, and if you prune too hard the plant could die.

√ Never remove more than one-third of the total plant foliage at any one time which can result in too much stress on the plant.

√ The best time to prune is when a plant is dormant. Pruning in late summer or early fall can result in a flush of new growth with not enough time to harden off for winter dormancy. Late pruning can invigorate a plant at a time it should be going dormant, making it vulnerable to winter-kill injury.

Pruning Pines

Pines are somewhat unique in their pruning requirements. Trees may be limbed up or branches cut back when the plants are dormant.

Limbing up can be used to accentuate the trees form, bark coloring or characteristics (such as exfoliating or patterned bark).

"Candling" is a special technique used to control the overall plant size. In the spring, the pine buds swell and new growth pushes out into a long slender "candle." The new needles are tightly pressed along the stem at first. After several days, the needles start to expand and push away from the stem. This is the best time to prune. Simply break off the top 1/2 to 2/3's of the candle with your fingers. Use your fingers — not pruners - to prune the candles — pruners cut the needle tips which will turn brown if damaged by cutting. Continue to break the candles over the entire tree to restrict the new flush of growth. The result will be a bushier, more compact specimen.

Reversions

Reversions are usually vigorous attempts by the plant to return to the "species form" of the plant. Some dwarf clones are more stable than others and never revert, while some clones, for example, cultivars of Sawara moss cypress (*Chamaecyparis pisifera*) are always attempting to revert.

A good knowledge of the growth habit of your particular cultivar will enable you to spot a renegade branch quickly. When pruning out reversions, make your cut in the stable growth a little beyond where the reversion occurs. This will ensure that you have removed the area where the reversion originated.

Candling

above. – An effective pruning method for pines.
Photos by Susan Martin

Reversions

below. Susan Martin showing rampant growth on a selection of *Pinus strobus*. When a cultivar's yearly growth rate is 1-2"/yr – and there is a growth spurt of 6-10" – it is a reversion that should be pruned out. Photo courtesy of USNA

Pests and Diseases

When growing conditions create stress for the plant, pest and diseases are more prevalent. Stress can be from prolonged drought, too much rain over too long a period, extreme cold periods without adequate protection, etc. However, most conifers are adapted to a wide variety of conditions and tolerate marginal conditions quite well. Because of the small size of most dwarf and slow-growing conifers, detection and treatment of most pests and diseases is a relatively simple matter.

The key to managing pest problems is early detection. Weekly visits to your conifer planting with pests in mind will go far to help you keep things under control. Scheduled sprays based only on calendar dates are often only marginally effective because pest and disease appearance is subject to the vagaries of the weather. Treatment to control a particular pest shortly after it has been sighted in the garden is most effective for the same reason. A close periodic check for pests and their development can calm your fears and reduce the amount of pesticide treatment that will be necessary.

Ground-hugging cultivars need to be checked regularly for fungal problems which are encouraged by damp conditions. Long periods of wet weather accentuate any problem with fungal diseases. Good air circulation (often requiring judicious pruning) discourages this problem.

Tight-foliage cultivars (especially spruce and hemlock) can be susceptible to spider-mite attacks, particularly in dry weather. A forceful hosing of the foliage once a week helps keep them pest free. If you do get an infestation, prompt treatment is essential.

Integrated Pest Management (IPM)

- Is a logical system of pest control

- Recognizes that pests exist in every environment including public gardens and nurseries.

- Involves carefully monitoring your landscape plants to detect pest problems before there is long-term damage.

- Utilizes both chemical and non-chemical control options to manage pest and disease damage.

- Saves time and money. Alternatives to pesticides are usually the preferred choice. This saves money on costly treatments and time spent on spraying.

- Causes minimal damage to the environment. IPM works with the natural ecology of the landscape to minimize pest damage.

Insect Pests

Bagworms — Are caterpillars that defoliate many different conifers. They are particularly damaging to *Juniperus, Thuja* and *Picea.* They protect and camouflage themselves with a cone-shaped, extremely strong silken case with bits of the plant material they are feeding on stuck to the outside. Sometimes these cases are mistaken for cones. The bagworms overwinter as eggs inside the female cases. The eggs hatch in late spring, and the tiny caterpillars immediately start to construct their protective case. As the caterpillars mature, they have a ravenous appetite and can easily defoliate even large plants.

Control of this pest is relatively simple. You can remove and crush the tell-tale bags any time of the year. You may need to cut them off with a pair of scissors since the silk strand that attaches the bag to the

Bagworm damage Photo by Susan Martin

plant is very strong. If the caterpillars are too numerous to remove by hand, treat the plant with an insecticide containing *Bacillus thuringiensis* as soon as the young caterpillars are seen.

Spider Mites — Are spider relatives: They pierce the needles, then suck the sap out of them. This results in a very fine stipple pattern that is hard to detect on the plant. Spider mites are damaging to many conifers grown in hot, dry, or dusty conditions. In severe infestations, the mites spin a webby material. The mites spread in the wind, and may congregate on the webs they spin waiting for the wind or a passing animal to break the web off and transport them to a new host plant. Severe infestations may quickly turn a plant yellow or even brown, and needle drop may result.

Mite damage   Photo by Scott Aker

To minimize mite damage, plant your conifers in a site that is not too hot and dry for the particular species you are planting.

You can physically remove the mites with a strong stream of water. Because they do not have wings and the distance they can crawl is limited, they cannot return to infest the plant again.

Lacewings, beneficial insects with pale green or brown, delicate, transparent lacy wings twice the size of their bodies, are often very important in controlling mites. Predatory mites that feed on the mites damaging the plant can be purchased and are very effective as long as temperatures are warm and humidity is high.

Horticultural oil is very effective in controlling severe infestations since it kills all stages of the mite including the eggs. It is a contact insecticide, so thorough coverage of all surfaces of the plant is essential.

To detect mites, try beating a branch of the plant over a white sheet of paper. The mites will appear on the paper as small red or black specks the size of black pepper flakes. The mites will move on the paper if temperatures are warm.

Spruce spider mites are similar in every respect to other spider mites, but they prefer cooler weather and will appear in spring and fall. Their control is the same as for other spider mites.

Pine Tip Moths - As the name suggests, pine tip moths attack only pines. The Nantucket pine tip moth is an especially serious pest of dwarf pines since it is a weak flyer and can only fly five feet or less from the ground. It is perfectly adapted to attack dwarf and prostrate pines. The tip moths overwinter as pupae inside the tips of pines that were damaged in the previous season. Most of the tip moths have two generations per year in all but the most northern states. Adults emerge from

Pine tip moth damage on *Pinus banksiana*   Photo by Susan Martin

Conifers Coming of Age
Insect Pests

IPM at the U.S. National Arboretum

Since the development of the IPM program in 1992, pesticide use has been reduced by over 70%.

Biorational pesticides such as horticultural oil, insecticidal soap, and insect growth regulators have been utilized more frequently and are far less toxic. Plant collections are carefully monitored on a regular basis to catch pest outbreaks before damage is significant.

Instead of spraying entire groups of plants, only those affected are treated. Egg masses are removed before insects are able to hatch, beneficial insects are released to feed on damaging pests and everyone makes a conscious effort to handle sanitation property.

IPM & Juniper Scale
Note from Scott Aker

I searched high and low for juniper scale. It's at its worst in the busy spring season and I neglected to get a photo early on in the IPM Program. About all I could find were a few pathetic scale covers that apparently had been riddled by parasitic wasps last year. We've not had to spray a single plant in the last year for juniper scale and it was our second most prevalent problem (behind mites) when I started.

the tips in mid spring to mate. The females lay eggs on the needles near the tips of the pine foliage and the tiny caterpillars begin their life by chewing their way down the needle until they reach the young, developing pine shoot. They spend the rest of their lives tunneling in the tender shoot and terminal bud of the shoot, where they cause extensive damage. In severe cases, they may kill nearly every shoot on a small pine, disfiguring it or causing it to decline.

Two and three needled pines are the only pines seriously affected by pine tip moths. *Pinus sylvestris*, *P. mugo*, and *P. resinosa* are favored hosts of the Nantucket pine tip moth. Other pines may be affected by other species of tip moths, but they do not occur as frequently and do not cause as much damage.

The most successful control is to simply remove the damaged tips of pines in early spring before the adults emerge. If the pupa is exposed to the elements, it will not survive. If this kind of preening and grooming is impractical for your situation, your only other alternative is chemical control.

Timing is the key to chemical control of this pest. Look carefully in late spring and early summer for eggs that may have been laid on the needles and signs of the young caterpillars chewing down the young needles toward the tip or candle growth. At this early stage, many relatively non-toxic pesticides such as *Bacillus thuringiensis* are effective. Once the caterpillars have entered the bud, they must be treated with a harsher systemic pesticide such as dimethoate.

Juniper Scale and Related Scales — Chalky white juniper scales can appear in such high numbers that they make the plant appear flocked. Like mites, they suck the sap out of the plant, causing it to turn yellow and lack vigor.

Juniper and related scales overwinter as mature adults or eggs under the tough white scale covers. The hatchlings, called crawlers, are about the same size as mites and can be easily detected by beating a branch of the infested plant over a white sheet of paper. They are usually amber or yellow in color. The crawlers are small enough to be caught in the wind where they can spread to new host plants. The juniper scale then settles down in the spot where it will spend the rest of its life and immediately exudes a protective cover that it enlarges as it grows.

Juniper scale is particularly fond of *Juniperus communis* and its cultivars. It is also a problem on *J. scopulorum* and its cultivars. Other junipers are affected but do not support such severe infestations as these two groups of junipers. Similar species of scale are sometimes a problem on Leyland cypress, *Thuja*, and *Cryptomeria*.

The best way to control scale is to smother them with an horticultural oil spray when all the crawlers have hatched. Begin beat-testing plants in May to determine when the crawlers are present. Check plants at least once every week. As soon as crawlers are detected, chart their numbers. When the number of crawlers you detect in your weekly check has peaked and begun to decline, it is the right time to spray the oil. Be sure to check for beneficial insects such as the small black sap beetles, small black beneficial wasps and lacewings that may appear in the beat tests as well. Do not spray plants if these beneficials appear with the crawlers.

Eriophyid Rust Mites – This microscopic pest can very seriously damage hemlocks, spruces, and more recently, bald cypress. Most gardeners completely overlook this pest since it is so small. You can beat-test using a white sheet of paper to find them, but you will definitely need a jeweler's loupe or some other magnification equal to or greater than 20× (about 40× is best) to clearly see this pest. Under magnification, they look like small yellow to orange carrot shaped objects with only two pairs of legs.

Distantly related to the spider mites, they prefer cool weather like the spruce spider mite. Eriophyids may appear in large numbers on spruces and hemlocks as early as March if the weather has remained above freezing for an extended period of time. They can reproduce rapidly, but their population collapses for unknown reasons in early summer. Little is known about the life history of this pest.

Eriophyids produce a microscopic stippling that is not visible to the naked eye. Plants show damage by turning off-color. Initially, the plant looks darker green, and this early damage is often misinterpreted as good health. With heavy damage, the color progresses to yellow-green and finally a rusty-brown color. Needle drop follows severe damage.

When large numbers of eriophyids are detected, they may be controlled as the other mites are with predatory mites, a strong stream of water, or horticultural oil. In addition, insecticidal soap is quite effective in controlling this mite. Begin your beat-testing to detect this mite in early March.

> ### Integrated Pest Mangagment
>
> It doesn't matter whether your garden is as large as an arboretum or as small as a windowsill, IPM can improve the way your plants look and grow.

Eriophyid rust mite – hemlock.
Photo by Scott Aker

Eriophyid rust mite – bald cypress
Photo by Scott Aker

Conifers Coming of Age
Insect Pests

Arborvitae leaf minor damage
Photo by Scott Aker

Juniper tip midge damage
Photo by Scott Aker

Hemlock woolly adelgid damage
Photo by Susan Martin

Springtails — Though not listed as a pest in any insect reference, these evolutionarily ancient insects are often associated with browning of new growth on the tightest-growing and dwarfest of the dwarf conifers. They are seldom seen on larger plants. It is not known with certainty if the springtails are feeding on the damaged tissue, but their large numbers in conjunction with the damage would seem to indicate that they are responsible. You can find springtails by beat testing in the same way you would test for mites. They are small oblong wingless insects with long antennae that prefer to crawl around but can also hop if startled. Large populations of springtails are effectively controlled by a single application of insecticidal soap.

Juniper Tip Midges and Arborvitae Leaf Miners — Juniper tip midges are small gnat-like flies that lay eggs in the tip growth of junipers. The maggot-like larvae burrow around in the tips and cause them to turn brown. Arborvitae leaf miners are moths that lay eggs near the tip growth of *Thuja*. Small caterpillars hatch from the eggs and tunnel around in the tip growth.

To check for midges or miners, carefully break open the branch tip and examine it for the larvae of either pest. Both of these pests can be easily managed with light shearing to remove the damaged tips. If shearing is not possible, a systemic insecticide can be used.

Hemlock Woolly Adelgid - These aphid relatives have created a stir in the conifer world and some designers are avoiding the use of *Tsuga* in their plans because of the damage and death caused by this foreign pest. The woolly adelgid sucks the juices out of the needles, resulting in lack of vigor, yellowing, and needle drop. Large populations can kill plants in one or two seasons.

The good news is that you can grow *Tsuga* very successfully, even when this pest is present. It is essential that *Tsuga* be planted in a site that gives the plant at least a minimum of light shade and moist soil. Often death that is blamed on the hemlock woolly adelgid is actually caused by a three-pronged attack from elongate hemlock scale, erio-phyid mites and the adelgid. The adelgid has an immensely complex life cycle. Sometimes it also attacks spruces, typically late in the season. Adelgid crawlers appear late in spring, and control efforts are most successful at this time of year when the insect lacks its covering of waxy white wool.

Begin beat-testing to find the small, oval brownish black crawlers in late April. Crawlers may hatch over a long period of time, so it is important to delay treatment until most of them have hatched. Shortly after hatching, they come to rest on the needles, where they feed for a short time. They then move to the base of the needle and develop their typical fuzzy white wool. This pest is vulnerable in the crawler and settled crawler stages. Very thorough treatment with horticultural oil or insecticidal soap are highly effective in these stages.

Sawflies - Damage a wide variety of pines. By far the most common, the red-headed pine sawfly appears in October and can quickly defoliate small plants. The less common white pine sawfly appears in the spring and again in the fall. Although they look like caterpillars, sawflies are actually more closely related to bees and wasps. They like to feed in large groups and prefer to completely strip a single branch before moving on to the next one. The larvae pupate on the ground and the bee-like adults lay their eggs in neat rows in the needles.

Sawflies   *Photo by Scott Aker*

Control of this pest can be simple. If you find the eggs (neat, evenly spaced protrusions on the needle), you can simply remove the needles carrying the eggs. Even after they have hatched, you can take advantage of their gregarious behavior and simply remove the whole group of catapillers from the plant.

Diseases

Needle Cast Diseases - Are fungi that cause conifers to drop or cast large numbers of needles. Pines and spruces are most commonly affected. This needle drop usually takes place in the spring or summer and should not be confused with the normal loss of interior needles that takes place every fall.

Most needle cast fungi are favored by prolonged periods of wet weather. Poor air circulation is often present when needle cast is a routine problem. Plants should be spaced appropriately and branches can be thinned to improve air circulation. Fallen needles can be cleaned up to reduce the inoculum of the fungus available to cause new infections. Needle casts do not affect the buds of the plant, so the plant can replace damaged foliage with new needles.

Ploioderma needle cast disease –
Pinus thunbergiana   *Photo by Scott Aker*

Fungicide treatment is usually not advisable unless you are trying to save a plant that has a history of the disease. If you feel that treatment is necessary, spray the plant with a broad-spectrum fungicide after the small spots indicating active infections are noted on the lower needles. Continue weekly treatment until the weather is dry.

Conifers Coming of Age
Diseases

Phomopsis tip blight – Juniper
Photo by Scott Aker

Cytspora canker – Blue Spruce
Photo by Scott Aker

Diplodia tip blight damage – *Pinus sylvestris*   Photo by Susan Martin

Cercospora blight – Cryptomeria
Photo by Scott Aker

Juniper Tip and Twig Blights - Fungal blights are commonly a problem on low-growing ground cover junipers. Dead tip growth appears in the summer as a result of *Phomopsis* and similar damage can occur earlier in the season as a result of *Kabatina* infection. Many resistant cultivars of junipers show little damage from either disease. If it becomes a problem, dead areas can be pruned out. Fungicide treatment is usually not needed since the junipers can easily recover from light or moderate damage. Heavy damage only occurs in situations where the juniper cultivar is a susceptible one and is growing in poor conditions.

Canker Diseases - Cankers are seldom a problem with dwarf conifers. Spruces may sometimes be affected, and Cytospora is common on Colorado blue spruce. Rigorous pruning of blighted branches is the only effective control. Typically, damage starts low on the skirt of the spruce and progresses upward. Cytospora appears to be a less frequent problem on dwarf forms of blue spruce.

Diplodia Tip Blight - This fungus can be devastating or fatal to many two and three needled pines. It causes the new tip growth to die and eventually entire branches may die. Austrian and Scots pines are particularly susceptible. Winter pruning of dead branches and complete removal of dead tips will greatly reduce the severity of the disease. The spores splash upward in spring rains, so the disease has a tendency to spread slowly upward on the plant over a period of several years. Pines growing in more exposed and isolated positions are much less affected than pines growing in crowded conditions.

If your pines have been damaged by diplodia tip blight, fungicide treatment may be necessary to save the plant. Timing is essential – In the spring, it is important to watch the candle growth. Apply a fungicide to the candles when they are fully elongated and the needles have just begun to grow through the sheath. Apply the fungicide again when the needles are half grown, usually about 10 days later.

Cercospora Blight - is damaging only to *Cryptomeria* and some junipers. It can be easily distinguished by the purple-brown cast it gives to the affected branches. Infections generally are worse on lower and interior branches. A band of purple may appear on the stem and the foliage above the band will eventually turn brown and die.

Pruning out dead foliage often helps to limit damage from this disease, and usually opens the plant up to better air circulation. Monthly fungicide treatment may help to alleviate severe infections. Treat plants every one to two weeks beginning in March until weather has turned warm and dry.

Susceptible Drought-Stressed Pines

Although two and three needled pines are drought adapted, you should give them extra water if drought prevails in the summer, especially if the weather is hot. Drought stressed pines often attract pine sawyers that carry deadly pine-wood nematodes. Once the pine sawyer has infected your pine with nematodes, there is little you can do. Pines that are infected with nematodes die quickly. The nematodes stop the production of resin, so there is little or no resin left in the wood.

To determine if a tree died from nematodes, cut a section of wood, then soak it in water to detect the nematodes. Using magnification, they can be seen streaming out of the wood. Often blue stain fungus accompanies the nematodes and the wood inside the tree becomes gray-blue in color. Promptly destroy any plants that are killed by nematodes. Fortunately, pine sawyers refuse to feed on healthy trees, so you are unlikely to encounter a problem if you start with the right growing conditions.

IPM for Winter (Winter Clean-up)

Winter is a good time for sanitation. The loss of some of the needles in the fall can make dead tips, crowded branches, and wounds easier to see. Remove all dead material and clean up fallen needles if tip blight or needle cast has been a problem.

Thin branches that are too crowded and remove badly wounded branches.

Collect cones from plants that have tip blight and burn them in the fireplace since they often carry large numbers of spores.

Summary

Keep in mind the introduction to this chapter, "Conifers are known to be among the toughest, most cold-hardy evergreens, and are considered the backbone and 'work-horses' of the garden." Also the beginning to the maintenance section in this chapter, "One of the benefits of growing dwarf conifers is that they only require minimal maintenance."

With both of these thoughts in mind, realize that in the "normal" home garden situation, you are not likely to run into very many of the problems mentioned. The U.S. National Arboretum has experienced most all of the problems in one way or another, at one time or another, due to the large concentrations of the collections. Another factor is the

Cercospora blight – Cryptomeria
Photo by Scott Aker

Predatory Mites and Wasps

"How can we tell the predatory mites and wasps from the pests? Can I get photos?"

I asked this question of Christy Brown, IPM Intern. Her answer was that they are so tiny you need a magnifying glass to recognize them, making photos difficult without special equipment. But the differences are simple to recognize:

Predatory mites move quickly; they're looking for food. Pest mites are slow – they sit & suck! Predatory wasps are slim, shaped like a wasp, and are about the size of a gnat.

Scott Aker confirmed this, explaining further that there are hundreds of species of predatory wasps – there are far more of the gnat-size wasps than of the 'common' size wasp most people are familiar with. He went on to explain that most wasps are the 'good guys'!

Summary - Continued

Scott Aker

Scott Aker is the Horticulturist in charge of the Integrated Pest Management Program at the U.S. National Arboretum in Washington, DC. He holds a Master's Degree in Horticulture from the University of Maryland and a Bachelor's Degree in Horticulture from the University of Minnesota.

A native of the Black Hills of western South Dakota, Scott served for a short time with the University of Maryland Cooperative Extension Service in Howard County, Maryland after completing his Master's thesis. He has served in internships with Monsanto, Northrup King Seeds, and Longwood Gardens.

Scott lives in Laurel, Maryland with his wife and twin two-year old sons amidst a half-acre garden that is constantly under development.

time period of thirty plus years that the Gotelli Collection has been under the care of the U.S. National Arboretum.

My hope is that when you do encounter problems with your conifers, that the combined experience and expertise of Susan Martin and Scott Aker will help you recognize and solve those problems. I must again most sincerely thank both Susan and Scott for sharing this information.

The majority of the Care and Maintenance portion of this chapter was contributed by Susan Martin, Curator of The Gotelli, Watnong and Dogwood Collections at the U.S. National Arboretum. I gleaned and consolidated this helpful information from various articles and handouts she had published and graciously encouraged me to use in this book "... if it would help"!

The Pests and Diseases portion of this chapter was written and contributed by Scott Aker, Integrated Pest Management Coordinator at the U.S. National Arboretum.

Bibliography
and
Recommended Reading

American Conifer Society Bulletin - ACS Office, P.O. Box 519, Chelsea, MI 48118-0519 FAX (313) 433-5442

Bagust, Harold. *"The Gardener's Dictionary of Horticultural Terms"*. London, England: Cassell Publishers Limited, 1992.

Bergman, Helene M., ed. *"Dwarf Conifers"* - *Plants & Gardens, Brooklyn Botanic Garden Record* (Brooklyn Botanic Gardens, Inc.) 21, no.1 New York: 1965.

Bloom, Adrian. *"**Conifers for Your Garden**"*. New York: Charles Scribner's Sons, 1972.

Coombes, Allen J. *"Dictionary of Plant Names"*. United Kingdom: Newnes Books — Portland, Oregon: Timber Press, 1985.

Den Ouden, P. & Boom, B.K. *"Manual of Cultivated Conifers"*. Netherlands: The Hague/Martinus Nijhoff, 1965.

Harrison, Charles R. *"**Ornamental Conifers**"*. First published Wellington, New Zealand: A.H. & W.W. Reed Limited — New York: Hafner Press, 1975.

Hillier Nurseries. *"The Hillier Manual of Trees and Shrubs"*, 6th ed. Newton Abbot: David & Charles Ltd., 1992.

Krüssman, Gerd. *"Manual of Cultivated Conifers"*. 2nd, rev. ed. Portland, Oregon: Timber Press, 1985, c1983.

*Rushforth, Keith D. "**Conifers**". Facts on File, Inc., 1987.*

Stearn, W.T. & E.R. *"A Gardener's Dictionary of Plant Names"*. London, England: Cassell Publishers Limited, 1992.

Van Gelderen, D.M. and J.R.P. van Hoey Smith. *"**Conifers**"*. Portland, Oregon: Timber Press, 1986.

Van Gelderen, D.M. and J.R.P. van Hoey Smith. *"**Conifers**, The Illustrated Encyclopedia - Two Volumes"*. Timber Press, 1996.

Welch, Humphrey J. *"Dwarf Conifers: A Complete Guide"*. Newton, Massachusetts: Charles T. Branford Company, 1966.

Further Recommended Reading

Key:

(gen.) = general descriptions, information and garden care

(spec.) = species identification and information

Bolded = especially recommended by author for examples of dwarf and unusual conifers

Appleton, Bonnie Lee. *"Trees, Shrubs and Vines"* - *Rodale's Successful Organic Gardening*. Weldon Russell Pty Ltd, 1993. (gen.)

Bärtels, Andreas. *"Gardening With Dwarf Trees and Shrubs"*. Translation by Timber Press - Portland, Oregon, 1986. (gen.)

Bloom, Alan & Adrian. *"Blooms of Bressingham Garden Plants"*. Great Britain: HarperCollins Manufacturing - New York: HarperCollins Publishers, 1992. (gen.) **(See –** Bloom, Adrian. *"**Conifers"** p.150)

Bond, John & Randall, Lyn. *"**Dwarf and Slow-growing Conifers"**. The Royal Horticultural Society - A Wisley Handbook. London: Cassell Educational Limited, 1987. (gen.)

Carr, David. *"**Heathers & Conifers"** - *Crowood Gardening Guides*. The Crowood Press Ltd., 1991. (gen.)

Constable, George, ed. *"Evergreen Shrubs"* - *Time-Life Gardener's Guide*. Time-Life Books, 1989. (gen.)

Coombes, Allen J. *"Trees"* - *Eyewitness Handbook*. London, Great Britain: Dorling Kindersley Limited, 1992. (spec.)

Cresson, Charles O. *"Ornamental Trees"* - *Burpee American Gardening Series*. Prentice Hall, 1993. (gen.)

Dirr, Michael. *"All About Evergreens"*. Ortho Books, 1984. (gen.)

Erler, Catriona Tudor. *"Trees & Shrubs"* - *Step-by-Step Successful Gardening*. Meridith Books, 1995. (gen.)

Fell, Derek. *"Trees & Shrubs"*. HP Books, 1986. (gen.)

Ferguson, Barbara, ed. *"All About Trees"*. Ortho Books, 1992. (gen.)

Fine Gardening, The Best of. *"Shrubs & Trees"*. The Taunton Press, 1993. (gen.) **(See –** Raulston, J.C. *"**Eastern Red Cedar"** p.85 & Fincham, Robert. *"**Dwarf Conifers"** p.89)

Garden Club of America, The. *"Plants That Merit Attention"*, Volume 1, Trees. Portland, Oregon: Timber Press, 1984, reprinted 1994. (gen.)

Gates, Galen...[et al.]. *"Shrubs and Vines"* - *The American Garden Guides*. Pantheon Books, 1994.(gen.)

Heriteau, Jacueline. *"The National Arboretum Book of Outstanding Garden Plants"*. The Stonesong Press, Inc., 1990. (spec.)

Knight, Frank...[et al.]. *"**Heathers, Conifers and the Winter Garden"**. Cassell/ The Royal Horticultural Society, 1995. (gen.)

Mitchell, Alan & More, David. *"The Trees of North America"*. New York: Facts on File, Inc., 1987. (spec.)

Obrizok, Robert A. *"**A Garden of Conifers"**. Deer Park, Wisconsin: Capability's Books, 1994. (gen.)

Phillips, Roger. *"Trees of North America and Europe"*. London: Pan Books Ltd. - New York: Random House, 1978. (spec.)

Pielou, E.C. *"The World of Northern Evergreens"*. Ithica, NY: Comstock Publishing Associates, 1988. (spec.)

Proudley, Brian & Valerie. *"**Garden Conifers in Colour"**. Poole, Dorset, UK: Blandford Press, 1976. (gen.)

Ritter, Francis, ed. *"Garden Trees"* - *Eyewitness Garden Handbooks*. New York, NY: DK Publishing, Inc. 1996. (gen.) **(See – Conifers** Large, Medium, Small & Dwarf, pgs 122-163)

Thomas, William R., ed. *"Trees & Shrubs"* - *Hearst Garden Guides*. The Hearst Corporation, 1992. (gen.)

Tripp, Kim E. & Raulston, J.C. *"The Year in Trees, Superb Woody Plants for Four-Season Gardens"*. Portland, Oregon: Timber Press, 1995. (gen.)

Wilson, Jim. *"Masters of the Victory Garden"*. Canada: Little, Brown and Company, 1990. (gen.) **(See –** Rezek, Ed. *"**Dwarf Conifers"** p.135)

Wilson, Jim and Sternberg, Guy. *"Landscaping with Native Trees"*. Chapters Publishing Ltd., 1995. (spec.)

Glossary

ACS - American Conifer Society

Acute - sharp-pointed

Adpressed - pressed into close contact without adhering

Alba, albus - white

Alternate - leaves or banches which do not grow out opposite one another

Apex - top terminating point of a leaf or tree

Ascending - directed or rising upward

Aril - fleshy seed holder — glutinous covering that envolopes certain seeds, like the yew berry

Awl - sharp, pointed instrument for boring holes

Axil - angle between branch and branchlet or branchlet & leaf

Aurea - golden

Break - to branch; to send out new shoots from dormant wood

Columnar - narrow cylindrical, column-like

Conical - cone-shaped

Cultivar - plant only found in cultivation

Cuspidata - with a sharp stiff point

Deciduous - loosing leaves for a season

Dioecious - having male & female flowers on separate plants

Dwarf Conifer - a conifer that never attains the stature which is considered normal for plants of its original species, variety or cultivar; a cultivar that will attain only a fraction of the full growth of its species.

Evergreen - retaining leaves year-round

Fastigiate - tall, columnar, growing upright; branches rising vertically close to main stem; with branches close together & erect, often forming a column (fastigiate forms tend to split open during winter weather—burlapping or binding helps prevent winter damage)

FONA - Friends of the National Arboretum

Glauca, Glaucous - grey or bluish 'bloom' on foliage

Lateral - emerging from the side

Nomenclature - systematic naming & classification of plants

Ogon - golden

Pendulous - drooping downward

Plumosa - feathery

Prostrata - doesn't have a leader — no backbone — sprawls on the ground

Prostrate - lying flat on the ground

Pyramidal - broad-based, tapering evenly towards the tip

Radial - similar petals which radiate symmetrically from a common central point

Radiate - spreading from a common center point

Stomatic - bands of 'breathing poses' (stoma) on the foliage, usually grey or white

Strike - to root

Strobulus - cone- or catkin-like arrangement of male and female flowers

Taxonomy - science of identification, nomenclature & classification of objects

Type - normal form of a plant

USNA - United States National Arboretum

Whorl - circle of 3 or more leaves at one node, like the spokes of a wheel & originating from stem or axis at the same level

Witch's-broom - an abnormal dense growth of branchlets on one portion of a plant

This glossary provides a quick reference for many of the terms used in this book. For further help, either - or both - Bagust's and Stearn's dictionaries are quite thorough. Stearn's is strictly a dictionary, quite extensive, with almost no illustrations, but does include a 30-page listing by common names. Bagust's has detailed drawings throughout, plus a 10-page appendix with drawings illustrating various botanical forms, propagation, budding & grafting methods. I use both of them. Their approach is so different, that what you don't find in one, you'll usually find in the other. And when you do find what you're looking for in one, the other will often give a different insight.

Bagust, Harold, *The Gardener's Dictionary of Horticultural Terms*, Cassell Publishers Limited, London, 1992

Stearn, William T., *Stearn's Dictionary of Plant Names for Gardeners, A Handbook on the Origin and Meaning of the Botanical Names of Some Cultivated Plants*, Cassell Publishers Limited, London, 1992

Common - *Botanical*

> The number in the parentheses ( ) following the various Pine species indicates the number of needles in a cluster.

Alaska Cypress — *Chamaecyparis nootkatensis*

Alberta Spruce — *Picea glauca*

Alcock's Spruce — *Picea bicolor*

American Arborvitae — *Thuja occidentalis*

Anglo-Japanese Yew — *Taxus x media*

Arborvitae — *Thuja*

Arizona Cypress — *Cupressus glabra*

Atlas Cedar — *Cedrus atlantica*

Austrian Pine (2) — *Pinus nigra*

Bald Cypress — *Taxodium distichum*

Balsam Fir — *Abies balsamea*

Bhutan Pine (5) — *Pinus wallichiana*

Black Pine (2) — *Pinus nigra*

Black Spruce — *Picea mariana*

Blue Pine (5) — *Pinus wallichiana*

Blue Spruce — *Picea pungens*

Bosnian Pine (2) — *Pinus leucodermis*

Bosnian Redcone Pine (2)
— *Pinus heldreichii var. leucodermis*

Canada Hemlock — *Tsuga canadensis*

Canadian Spruce — *Picea glauca*

Canton Water Pine — *Glyptostrobus lineatus*

Common - *Botanical* (Continued)

Cedar – *Cedrus*
Cedar of Lebanon – *Cedrus libani*
Chinese Golden Larch – *Pseudolarix amabilis*
Chinese Juniper – *Juniperus chinensis*
Chinese Lacebark Pine (3) – *Pinus bungeana*
Colorado Spruce – *Picea pungens*
Common Juniper – *Juniperus communis*
Creeping Juniper – *Juniperus horizontalis*
Dahurian Juniper – *Juniperus davurica*
Dawn Redwood – *Metasequoia glyptostroboides*
Douglas Fir – *Pseudotsuga menziesii*
East Siberian Fir – *Abies nephrolepis*
Eastern Red Cedar – *Juniperus virginiana*
Eastern White Pine (5) – *Pinus strobus*
English Yew – *Taxus baccata*
European Larch – *Larix decidua*
False Cypress – *Chamaecyparis*
Fir – *Abies*
Flaky or Scaly Juniper – *Juniperus squamata*
Giant Sequoia – *Sequoiadendron giganteum*
Golden Larch – *Pseudolarix amabilis*
Hemlock – *Tsuga*
Hiba Arborvitae – *Thujopsis dolabrata*
Himalayan Cedar – *Cedrus deodara*
Himalayan Pine – *Pinus wallichiana*
Hinoki Cypress – *Chamaecyparis obtusa*
Japanese Black Pine (2) – *Pinus thunbergiana*
Japanese Bush Spruce – *Picea maximowiczii*
Japanese Cedar – *Cryptomeria japonica*
Japanese Garden Juniper
    – *Juniperus procumbens*
Japanese Plum-Yew – *Cephalotaxus drupacea*
Japanese Red Pine (2) – *Pinus desiflora*
Japanese Stone Pine (5) – *Pinus pumila*
Japanese Umbrella Pine
    – *Sciadopitys verticillata*
Japanese White Pine (5) – *Pinus parviflora*
Japanese Yew – *Taxus cuspidata*
Juniper – *Juniperus*

Khingham Fir – *Abies nephrolepis*
Korean Pine (5) – *Pinus koraiensis*
Lacebark Pine (3) – *Pinus bungeana*
Larch – *Larix*
Lawson Cypress – *Chamaecyparis lawsoniana*
Leyland Cypress – *x Cupressocyparis leylandii*
Limber Pine (5) – *Pinus flexis*
Maidenhair Tree – *Ginkgo biloba*
Mountain Pine European (2) – *Pinus mugo*
Needle Juniper – *Juniperus rigida*
Nootka Cypress – *Chamaecyparis nootkatensis*
Northern Japanese Hemlock – *Tsuga diversifolia*
Norway Spruce – *Picea abies*
Oriental Arborvitae – *Platydladus orientalis*
Oriental Arborvitae – *Thujopsis dolabrata*
Oriental Spruce – *Picea orientalis*
Pencil Cedar – *Juniperus virginiana*
Pine – *Pinus*
Plum-Yew – *Cephalotaxus*
Red Pine (2) – *Pinus resinosa*
Redwood – *Sequoia sempervirens*
Rocky Mountain Juniper – *Juniperus scopulorum*
Sachalin Spruce – *Picea glehnii*
Savin Juniper – *Juniperus sabina*
Sawara Cypress – *Chamaecyparis pisifera*
Scots Pine (2) – *Pinus sylvestris*
Serbian Spruce – *Picea omorika*
Shore Juniper – *Juniperus conferta*
Shore Pine (2) – *Pinus contorta*
Siberian Carpet Cypress – *Microbiota decussata*
Silver Fir – *Abies alba*
Spanish Fir – *Abies pinsapo*
Spruce – *Picea*
Swamp Cypress – *Taxodium distichum*
Swiss Stone Pine (5) – *Pinus cembra*
Umbrella Pine, Japanese – *Sciadopitys verticillata*
Weymouth Pine (5) – *Pinus strobus*
White Cedar – *Chamaecyparis thyoides*
White Spruce – *Picea glauca*
Yew – *Taxus*

Botanical - **Common**

Abies – Fir
A. alba – Silver Fir
A. balsamea – Balsam Fir
A. nephrolepis – Khingham Fir – East Siberian Fir
A. pinsapo – Spanish Fir
Cedrus – Cedar
C. atlantica – Atlas Cedar
C. deodara – Himalayan Cedar
C. libani – Cedar of Lebanon
Cephalotaxus – Plum-Yew
C. drupacea – Japanese Plum-Yew
Chamaecyparis – False Cypress
C. lawsoniana – Lawson Cypress
C. nootkatensis – Nootka Cypress – Alaska Cypress
C. obtusa – Hinoki Cypress
C. pisifera – Sawara Cypress
C. thyoides – White Cedar
Cryptomeria japonica – Japanese Cedar
x Cupressocyparis leylandii – Leyland Cypress
Cupressus glabra – Arizona Cypress
Ginkgo biloba – Maidenhair Tree
Glyptostrobus lineatus – Canton Water Pine
Juniperus – Juniper
J. chinensis – Chinese Juniper
J. communis – Common Juniper
J. conferta – Shore Juniper
J. davurica – Dahurian Juniper
J. horizontalis – Creeping Juniper
J. procumbens – Japanese Garden Juniper
J. rigida – Needle Juniper
J. sabina – Savin Juniper
J. scopulorum – Rocky Mountain Juniper
J. squamata – Flaky or Scaly Juniper
J. virginiana – Eastern Red Cedar – Pencil Cedar
Larix – Larch
L. decidua – European Larch
Metasequoia glyptostroboides – Dawn Redwood
Microbiota decussata – Siberian Carpet Cypress
Picea – Spruce
P. abies – Norway Spruce
P. bicolor – Alcock's Spruce
P. glauca – White Spruce
    – Canadian Spruce – Alberta Spruce
P. glehnii – Sachalin Spruce
P. mariana – Black Spruce

P. maximowiczii – Japanese Bush Spruce
P. omorika – Serbian Spruce
P. orientalis – Oriental Spruce
P. pungens – Colorado Spruce – Blue Spruce
Pinus – Pine
P. bungeana – Chinese Lacebark Pine (3)
P. cembra – Swiss Stone Pine (5)
P. contorta – Shore Pine (2)
P. desiflora – Japanese Red Pine (2)
P. flexis – Limber Pine (5)
P. heldreichii var. leucodermis
    – Bosnian Redcone Pine (2)
P. koraiensis – Korean Pine (5)
P. leucodermis – Bosnian Pine (2)
P. mugo – Mountain Pine European (2)
P. nigra – Black Pine – Austrian Pine (2)
P. parviflora – Japanese White Pine (5)
P. pumila – Japanese Stone Pine (5)
P. resinosa – Red Pine (2)
P. strobus – Eastern White Pine – Weymouth Pine (5)
P. sylvestris – Scots Pine (2)
P. thunbergiana – Japanese Black Pine (2)
P. wallichiana – Himalayan Pine
    – Bhutan Pine – Blue Pine (5)
Platydladus orientalis – Oriental Arborvitae
Pseudolarix amabilis – Chinese Golden Larch
Pseudotsuga menziesii – Douglas Fir
Sciadopitys verticillata – Japanese Umbrella Pine
    – Umbrella Pine, Japanese
Sequoia sempervirens – Redwood
S. giganteum – Giant Sequoia
Taxodium distichum – Bald Cypress – Swamp Cypress
Taxus – Yew
T. baccata – English Yew
T. cuspidata – Japanese Yew
T. x media – Anglo-Japanese Yew
Thuja – Arborvitae
T. occidentalis – American Arborvitae
T. orientalis - see – *Platycladus orientalis*
Thujopsis dolabrata – Oriental Arborvitae
    – Hiba Arborvitae
Tsuga – Hemlock
T. canadensis – Canada Hemlock
T. diversifolia – Northern Japanese Hemlock

above: The variety of form outlines, textures and tonal differences can be easy to distinguish in black and white.

Index

above: Enjoy the huge variety of textures and forms that is apparent even without color − − And can you feel the summer haze muting the distinct outlines the same as it would be muting the dramatic differences in color? A color image of this scene is on page 2-7.

Photo by Susan Martin

Notes

Notes

Notes

Notes

Bookmark

Conifers Coming of Age

Common - *Botanical*

Alaska Cypress
 − *Chamaecyparis nootkatensis*
Alberta Spruce − *Picea glauca*
Alcock's Spruce − *Picea bicolor*
American Arborvitae
 − *Thuja occidentalis*
Anglo-Japanese Yew − *Taxus x media*
Arborvitae − *Thuja*
Arizona Cypress − *Cupressus glabra*
Atlas Cedar − *Cedrus atlantica*
Austrian Pine (2) − *Pinus nigra*
Bald Cypress − *Taxodium distichum*
Balsam Fir − *Abies balsamea*
Bhutan Pine (5) − *Pinus wallichiana*
Black Pine (2) − *Pinus nigra*
Black Spruce − *Picea mariana*
Blue Pine (5) − *Pinus wallichiana*
Blue Spruce − *Picea pungens*
Bosnian Pine (2) − *Pinus leucodermis*
Bosnian Redcone Pine (2)
 − *Pinus heldreichii var. leucodermis*
Canada Hemlock − *Tsuga canadensis*
Canadian Spruce − *Picea glauca*
Canton Water Pine
 − *Glyptostrobus lineatus*
Cedar − *Cedrus*
Cedar of Lebanon − *Cedrus libani*
Chinese Golden Larch
 − *Pseudolarix amabilis*
Chinese Juniper − *Juniperus chinensis*
Chinese Lacebark Pine (3)
 − *Pinus bungeana*
Colorado Spruce − *Picea pungens*
Common Juniper
 − *Juniperus communis*
Creeping Juniper
 − *Juniperus horizontalis*
Dahurian Juniper
 − *Juniperus davurica*
Dawn Redwood
 − *Metasequoia glyptostroboides*
Douglas Fir − *Pseudotsuga menziesii*
East Siberian Fir − *Abies nephrolepis*
Eastern Red Cedar
 − *Juniperus virginiana*
Eastern White Pine (5) − *Pinus strobus*
English Yew − *Taxus baccata*
European Larch − *Larix decidua*
False Cypress − *Chamaecyparis*
Fir − *Abies*
Flaky or Scaly Juniper
 − *Juniperus squamata*

Giant Sequoia
 − *Sequoiadendron giganteum*
Golden Larch − *Pseudolarix amabilis*
Hemlock − *Tsuga*
Hiba Arborvitae − *Thujopsis dolabrata*
Himalayan Cedar − *Cedrus deodara*
Himalayan Pine − *Pinus wallichiana*
Hinoki Cypress
 − *Chamaecyparis obtusa*
Japanese Black Pine (2)
 − *Pinus thunbergiana*
Japanese Bush Spruce
 − *Picea maximowiczii*
Japanese Cedar
 − *Cryptomeria japonica*
Japanese Garden Juniper
 − *Juniperus procumbens*
Japanese Plum-Yew
 − *Cephalotaxus drupacea*
Japanese Red Pine (2)
 − *Pinus desiflora*
Japanese Stone Pine (5)
 − *Pinus pumila*
Japanese Umbrella Pine
 − *Sciadopitys verticillata*
Japanese White Pine (5)
 − *Pinus parviflora*
Japanese Yew − *Taxus cuspidata*
Juniper − *Juniperus*
Khingham Fir − *Abies nephrolepis*
Korean Pine (5) − *Pinus koraiensis*
Lacebark Pine (3)
 − *Pinus bungeana*
Larch − *Larix*
Lawson Cypress
 − *Chamaecyparis lawsoniana*
Leyland Cypress
 − *x Cupressocyparis leylandii*
Limber Pine (5) − *Pinus flexis*
Maidenhair Tree − *Ginkgo biloba*
Mountain Pine European (2)
 − *Pinus mugo*
Needle Juniper − *Juniperus rigida*
Nootka Cypress
 − *Chamaecyparis nootkatensis*
Northern Japanese Hemlock
 − *Tsuga diversifolia*
Norway Spruce − *Picea abies*
Oriental Arborvitae
 − *Platydladus orientalis*
Oriental Arborvitae
 − *Thujopsis dolabrata*

Oriental Spruce − *Picea orientalis*
Pencil Cedar − *Juniperus virginiana*
Pine − *Pinus*
Plum-Yew − *Cephalotaxus*
Red Pine (2) − *Pinus resinosa*
Redwood
 − *Sequoia sempervirens*
Rocky Mountain Juniper
 − *Juniperus scopulorum*
Sachalin Spruce − *Picea glehnii*
Savin Juniper − *Juniperus sabina*
Sawara Cypress
 − *Chamaecyparis pisifera*
Scots Pine (2) − *Pinus sylvestris*
Serbian Spruce − *Picea omorika*
Shore Juniper − *Juniperus conferta*
Shore Pine (2) − *Pinus contorta*
Siberian Carpet Cypress
 − *Microbiota decussata*
Silver Fir − *Abies alba*
Spanish Fir − *Abies pinsapo*
Spruce − *Picea*
Swamp Cypress
 − *Taxodium distichum*
Swiss Stone Pine (5)
 − *Pinus cembra*
Umbrella Pine, Japanese
 − *Sciadopitys verticillata*
Weymouth Pine (5)
 − *Pinus strobus*
White Cedar
 − *Chamaecyparis thyoides*
White Spruce − *Picea glauca*
Yew − *Taxus*

> The number in the parentheses ( ) following the various Pine species indicates the number of needles in a cluster.

Bookmark

Conifers Coming of Age

Barton-Bradley Crossroads Publishing Co.

PO Box 802, North Olmsted, OH 44070-0802

Definitions – Relative Growth Rate/Size Guide*

Miniature Category is less than 3 inches growth per year.

    Expected size at 10 - 15 years would be 2 - 3 feet.

Dwarf Category is 3 - 6 inches growth per year.

    Expected size at 10 - 15 years would be 3 - 6 feet.

Intermediate Category is 6 - 12 inches growth per year.

    Expected size at 10 - 15 years would be 6 - 15 feet.

Large Category is over 12 inches growth per year.

    Expected size at 10 - 15 years would be over 15 feet.

*Resouce: The American Conifer Society web site:
http://www.pacificrim.net/~bydesign/acs.html

Definitions – Conifer Forms (Outlines)*

Globose – Rounded.

Pendulous – Upright or mounding with varying degrees of weeping branches.

Narrow Upright – Much taller than broad; includes fastigiate, columnar, narrowly pyramidal, or narrowly conical.

Broad Upright – Includes all other upright plants that do not fit into one of the above categories.

Prostrate – Ground-hugging, carpeting plants, lacking a central leader. The best have no tendency to grow upward, can include slightly mounding.

Spreading – Wider than tall, often includes mounding.

Irregular – Erratic growth pattern.

Culturally Altered – Pruned or trained into formal or imaginative shapes. Includes high grafts and standards.

Bookmark

Conifers Coming of Age

Botanical - Common

Abies – *Fir*
A. alba – *Silver Fir*
A. balsamea – *Balsam Fir*
A. nephrolepis – *Khingham Fir – East Siberian Fir*
A. pinsapo – *Spanish Fir*
Cedrus – *Cedar*
C. atlantica – *Atlas Cedar*
C. deodara – *Himalayan Cedar*
C. libani – *Cedar of Lebanon*
Cephalotaxus – *Plum-Yew*
C. drupacea – *Japanese Plum-Yew*
Chamaecyparis – *False Cypress*
C. lawsoniana – *Lawson Cypress*
C. nootkatensis – *Nootka Cypress – Alaska Cypress*
C. obtusa – *Hinoki Cypress*
C. pisifera – *Sawara Cypress*
C. thyoides – *White Cedar*
Cryptomeria japonica – *Japanese Cedar*
x Cupressocyparis leylandii – *Leyland Cypress*
Cupressus glabra – *Arizona Cypress*
Ginkgo biloba – *Maidenhair Tree*
Glyptostrobus lineatus – *Canton Water Pine*
Juniperus – *Juniper*
J. chinensis – *Chinese Juniper*
J. communis – *Common Juniper*
J. conferta – *Shore Juniper*
J. davurica – *Dahurian Juniper*
J. horizontalis – *Creeping Juniper*
J. procumbens – *Japanese Garden Juniper*
J. rigida – *Needle Juniper*
J. sabina – *Savin Juniper*
J. scopulorum – *Rocky Mountain Juniper*
J. squamata – *Flaky or Scaly Juniper*
J. virginiana – *Eastern Red Cedar – Pencil Cedar*
Larix – *Larch*
L. decidua – *European Larch*
Metasequoia glyptostroboides – *Dawn Redwood*
Microbiota decussata – *Siberian Carpet Cypress*
Picea – *Spruce*
P. abies – *Norway Spruce*
P. bicolor – *Alcock's Spruce*
P. glauca – *White Spruce*
   – Canadian Spruce – Alberta Spruce
P. glehnii – *Sachalin Spruce*
P. mariana – *Black Spruce*

P. maximowiczii – *Japanese Bush Spruce*
P. omorika – *Serbian Spruce*
P. orientalis – *Oriental Spruce*
P. pungens – *Colorado Spruce – Blue Spruce*
Pinus – *Pine*
P. bungeana – *Chinese Lacebark Pine (3)*
P. cembra – *Swiss Stone Pine (5)*
P. contorta – *Shore Pine (2)*
P. desiflora – *Japanese Red Pine (2)*
P. flexis – *Limber Pine (5)*
P. heldreichii var. leucodermis
   – Bosnian Redcone Pine (2)
P. koraiensis – *Korean Pine (5)*
P. leucodermis – *Bosnian Pine (2)*
P. mugo – *Mountain Pine European (2)*
P. nigra – *Black Pine – Austrian Pine (2)*
P. parviflora – *Japanese White Pine (5)*
P. pumila – *Japanese Stone Pine (5)*
P. resinosa – *Red Pine (2)*
P. strobus – *Eastern White Pine – Weymouth Pine (5)*
P. sylvestris – *Scots Pine (2)*
P. thunbergiana – *Japanese Black Pine (2)*
P. wallichiana – *Himalayan Pine*
   – Bhutan Pine – Blue Pine (5)
Platydladus orientalis – *Oriental Arborvitae*
Pseudolarix amabilis – *Chinese Golden Larch*
Pseudotsuga menziesii – *Douglas Fir*
Sciadopitys verticillata – *Japanese Umbrella Pine*
   – Umbrella Pine, Japanese
Sequoia sempervirens – *Redwood*
S. giganteum – *Giant Sequoia*
Taxodium distichum – *Bald Cypress – Swamp Cypress*
Taxus – *Yew*
T. baccata – *English Yew*
T. cuspidata – *Japanese Yew*
T. x media – *Anglo-Japanese Yew*
Thuja – *Arborvitae*
T. occidentalis – *American Arborvitae*
T. orientalis - *see* – Platycladus orientalis
Thujopsis dolabrata – *Oriental Arborvitae*
   – Hiba Arborvitae
Tsuga – *Hemlock*
T. canadensis – *Canada Hemlock*
T. diversifolia – *Northern Japanese Hemlock*

> The number in the parentheses ( ) following the various Pine species indicates the number of needles in a cluster.

Bookmark

Conifers Coming of Age

Barton-Bradley Crossroads Publishing Co.

PO Box 802, North Olmsted, OH 44070-0802

Definitions – Relative Growth Rate/Size Guide*

Miniature Category is less than 3 inches growth per year.

   Expected size at 10 - 15 years would be 2 - 3 feet.

Dwarf Category is 3 - 6 inches growth per year.

   Expected size at 10 - 15 years would be 3 - 6 feet.

Intermediate Category is 6 - 12 inches growth per year.

   Expected size at 10 - 15 years would be 6 - 15 feet.

Large Category is over 12 inches growth per year.

   Expected size at 10 - 15 years would be over 15 feet.

*Resouce: The American Conifer Society web site:
http://www.pacificrim.net/~bydesign/acs.html

Definitions – Conifer Forms (Outlines)*

Globose – Rounded.

Pendulous – Upright or mounding with varying degrees of weeping branches.

Narrow Upright – Much taller than broad; includes fastigiate, columnar, narrowly pyramidal, or narrowly conical.

Broad Upright – Includes all other upright plants that do not fit into one of the above categories.

Prostrate – Ground-hugging, carpeting plants, lacking a central leader. The best have no tendency to grow upward, can include slightly mounding.

Spreading – Wider than tall, often includes mounding.

Irregular – Erratic growth pattern.

Culturally Altered – Pruned or trained into formal or imaginative shapes. Includes high grafts and standards.

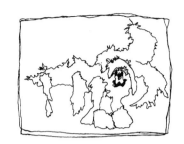

ORDER FORM

$40.00 U.S.

Dwarf & Unusual
Conifers Coming of Age
A Guide to Mature Garden Conifers

Sandra McLean Cutler

Name: _____

Address: _____

City: _____ State: _____ Zip: _____

Telephone: (____) _____

Sales tax:
Ohio residents only add sales tax 6%

Priority shipping and handling:
$6.75 per book

Payment:
Make Check or Money Order to:

Barton-Bradley Crossroads
Publishing Co.
P.O. Box 802
North Olmsted, OH 44070-0802

2023.071